Teenage Mothers Teenage Fathers

Anne Ross, R.N., R.T.

Teenage Mothers Teenage Fathers

PERSONAL LIBRARY
TORONTO

Personal Library, Publishers
Suite 439
17 Queen Street East
Toronto, Canada M5C 1P9

Publisher: Glenn Edward Witmer
Editor: Charis Wahl

The text illustrations are reproduced by courtesy of
Ortho Pharmaceutical (Canada) Ltd.

Distributed to the trade in Canada by
John Wiley and Sons Canada Limited
22 Worcester Road
Rexdale, Ontario M9W 1L1

Distributed to the trade in the United States by
Everest House
P.O. Box 978
424 Raritan Center
Edison, New Jersey 08817

Canadian Cataloguing in Publication Data

Ross, Anne (Anne G.)
   Teenage mothers/teenage fathers

ISBN 0-920510-39-6 pa.
     0-920510-53-1 cl.

1. Pregnancy, Adolescent.   2. Adolescent mothers.
3. Adolescent parents.   I. Title.

HV700.5.R67   362.8'39'088055   C81-094479-0

Printed and bound in Canada

To my husband, Bill, whose love, steadfastness,
understanding and support made everything
possible.

To my children, Dee Dee and Arthur, on whose
love and understanding I can always rely.

To Elizabeth Peterson, who encouraged me and
placed her professional skill at my disposal when
things were tough going.

CONTENTS

PREFACE

I was moved to write *Teenage Mothers/Teenage Fathers* because of my many encounters with the devastating effects of teenage pregnancy and parenting. This is an ever growing dilemma which needs to be dealt with much more effectively than is being done at the present time.

The problem has many aspects, but they fall into three main categories, and I have divided the book accordingly. The first section deals with the problem of teen sexuality, and the information, misinformation or lack of information teenagers are given by their parents, the medical profession, and society at large. The last element in this section is a short birth control guide indicating the advantages and disadvantages of various forms of contraception.

The second section of the book deals with the pregnant teenager and the various pressures on her—and the father of the unborn child—which influence the decision whether or not to carry the fetus to term.

The final category of the problem involves what to do with the child after it is born. What convinces a teenager that she should bring up the child herself rather than putting it up for adoption? What pressures are there on teenage marriages, and what complicating factors does a child bring to that relationship?

Finally we come, if not to complete solutions, at least to some recommendations for changing the situation. Given our medical resources and social services, changes could be made in a young mother's life to make her self-sufficient and self-supporting. Changes could also be made, so that every child raised by a teenage mother is a wanted child.

9

INTRODUCTION

The incidence of teenage pregnancies has been rising steadily. Those youngsters going to full term and keeping their babies has risen dramatically in the past ten years. The number of children bringing up children has almost doubled in numbers since 1968, in some cases, much higher. Some claim that this phenomenon has taken on epidemic proportions![1]

Over one million American teenagers become pregnant each year. More than 600,000 give birth. In the United States, ninety percent elect to keep their child. In Canada, eighty percent keep their babies. Births to females ten to fourteen years of age have nearly doubled. In 1957, there were 6,960 births to females ten to fourteen years old. In 1975, there were 12,642 births to that age group. And the figures are still rising. Teen and pre-teen births are not confined to any one population. They occur among young people of all ethnic and economic backgrounds. There are teenage and pre-teenage parents living in suburban and rural areas as well as in the inner city.

Seventy percent of these mothers get no medical care in the first three months of pregnancy. As a result, the death rate from complications of pregnancy, birth, and delivery for the fifteen to nineteen-year-old is thirteen percent greater than for mothers in their early twenties.[2] Moreover, infants born to teenage parents tend to have a low birth weight and a high incidence of birth injuries and childhood illnesses. Due to poor diet, inadequate prenatal care and immaturity of the endocrine system, the mortality rate for these children is two to three times that of children born to older mothers.

Introduction

The birth rate is decreasing all over the western world. Yet in all countries and in all socio-economic groups the rate for the fifteen to nineteen age group, especially single adolescent women as well as that of those under the age of fifteen, is increasing.

What is overwhelmingly concluded by various studies is that ninety-five percent of teenagers going to birth control clinics have experienced sexual intercourse without protection. We are looking at four million teenagers out there, many of whom may be pregnant and become child-mothers.[3]

Pregnancy is the reason most often cited by teenage females for discontinuing their education. Eighty percent of women who become mothers at seventeen or younger never complete high school. Fathers of children born to mothers fifteen and younger often are school dropouts; these young men have a higher unemployment rate than any other age or education group.

I have been involved with young people as a health worker and counselor for over twenty-five years. Never before has this problem been so widespread. The situation is dangerous both for the child-mother and her baby. For, in the main, children who keep their babies do so willy-nilly without realistic planning for the future.

Few have any concept of what is involved in parenting. They are usually lonely and often become desperate when faced with the harsh demands of child rearing. Outside of meager financial assistance, they are left to shift for themselves in a society that is indifferent or ignorant of their plight.

As yet, nothing of any consequence is being done in Canada to help these young mothers, who in the main have massive problems that are only exacerbated by having to care for a tiny bundle whose needs are constant. The child-mother, who is unable to cope, often vents her frustration in tragic acts of violence and abuse.

An American study has found that while unmarried families make up only sixteen percent of households, they account for fifty percent of reported abuse and neglect.[4]

The future of the child-mother and that of her baby looks bleak indeed. Both need care, guidance, and concerned assistance. Only the combined efforts of government educational and health departments and non-governmental health organizations can alleviate this problem.

Why is this happening?

It is not for want of trying by some agencies, clinics, and medical and

12

Introduction

nursing personnel. The failure of our educational system, the persistent propaganda by the pro-life groups, the scare stories which appear every now and again in the media, all combine to keep birth control information from teenagers, or present it in such a way as to make them view contraception as unacceptable.

A committee of the House of Representatives on population in the U.S.A. reported recently (April, 1979) that 4.2 million adolescents stand a chance of an unwanted pregnancy and 1.8 million (about forty-three percent) need but cannot get family planning assistance.

Where have we failed? How have we let these young people down? What should be done?

All these pregnancies do not have to occur. But once they do, what are the mother's options? If she decides to keep the baby, what are the pitfalls to be avoided? How can she learn to cope? How can she utilize existing social resources for her welfare and that of her helpless baby? It is my intent to give some answers.

---

[1] *Maclean's*, March 31st, 1980, p. 40.

[2] "For Your Information," Boston Hospital for Women Division of Affiliated Hospitals Center, Inc.

[3] In the U.S.A. the rate of adolescent childbearing is among the highest of any industrialized nation in the world. One of the factors compounding the problem is this country's increasing adolescent population. Over the last twenty-five years, the number of U.S. young people aged ten to nineteen has risen and now exceeds forty million. It is estimated that eleven million American teenagers are sexually active and of those, about one million adolescent girls—one in ten aged fifteen to nineteen become pregnant each year. Of these one million girls, 600,000 give birth and ninety percent keep their babies. Further, approximately 400,000 of the adolescent girls who give birth each year are seventeen years of age and under, including 30,000 who are fourteen years of age and under. It is these very young adolescents who face the greatest risk of a problem pregnancy. Statistics indicate that where prevention programs are not available, adolescents who give birth often become pregnant again quickly—forty-four percent within one year and seventy percent within two years.

[4] American Humane Society Study.

13

SECTION ONE
Let's Talk About It

"Where'd you go?"
"Out."
"What did you do?"
"Nothing."

We have to deal with first things first, so in this section we will look at teenage sexuality and how teenagers are taught—or not taught—to deal with it. We will also take a look at the role of the media in creating the image of teenagers, and to what extent this conforms with the statistics.

Next, we'll discuss teenagers' relations with parents and the other elements of society, particularly doctors, who come into contact with teenagers' sexual and moral dilemmas—and have their own dilemmas, too.

As a last word, we have included a brief outline of the menstrual cycle and the myths and methods of birth control: how *they work and if* they work.

1
ME, TOO

Shannon sat slouching in the chair, eyes downward; her brown, short hair unkempt; jeans torn at the cuff areas; her jacket full of grease spots. Her face still had some baby fat and her plumpish figure looked shapeless.

Her friend Judy was about a head taller—slim, dark blue eyes with a shag haircut, neatly combed, and wearing some makeup but not too much.

The difference between them was startling. Apparently they had been friends since grade one.

"Come on, Shannon, tell her—you know—about Doug."

"I can't."

"Don't be such a dopehead. How can you get straightened out if you are going to play dumb?"

"I'm not playing."

"OK, OK, I'm sorry. She thinks she's fat, ugly, and dumb so how can she have boyfriends? If she thinks so, they'll think so."

Out of the mouths of babes, I thought ruefully.

Shannon looked up for the first time and said, "Well, I am. I look in the mirror, too."

"Yah, but you won't do nothin' about it, just feel sorry for yourself."

"It's easy for you to talk—you have any guy you want."

"Big deal, so what—"

"So nothin', I wouldn't mind having just one."

"You can have them all."

"Sure, just like that."

"But, Shannon, you really are dumb. The first guy who pays her attention, she goes all the way."

"You do too, you told me."

"That's different. I know what I'm doing."

"Yah, so why were you afraid you got pregnant, too?"

"That was a mistake, I got drunk—you know that. I told you how it happened."

Shannon burst into tears. Judy, to my surprise, was trying to keep her tears from flowing.

I thrust Kleenex at them, sat close, and settled them down.

"Look, you two, how about one at a time."

Shannon began first. "All the kids in my class they all have boyfriends. Me, I never had one. So, on New Year's my neighbor friend and her brother had a party; their parents were out of town. So, she invited me. The crowd was older, like—they drank 'n all. This guy, he was real nice, he danced with me and was real nice. Everybody was doing it, you know, going upstairs—so I went too. He was real nice and he wanted, you know, to go all the way, so I did and it hurt but I didn't let on and he walked me home—that was nice and he kissed me good night and said he would call. But he never did."

"Is that why you thought you were pregnant?"

"Yah, I guess so." She looked forlorn again. "He never called or anything."

"She thinks she's ugly that's why he never called."

"Well, why didn't he? I did what he wanted, didn't I?"

"It doesn't always work." This piece of wisdom from Judy. "Y'know, the trouble with Shannon is that she thinks she's the only one who has problems. Being pretty—it doesn't help sometimes, you know.

"Well, here goes. My Mom and Dad separated when I was five. All I remember about him was that he was very big and real handsome. I loved him so much." Her tears were flowing freely. "Then he was gone. And Mom, well, I was the one she kinda clung to. I know it sounds queer but that's how it's been. And she was constantly running down Dad and all men. They were beasts, all bad, especially Dad. She worked and looked after me—that's it.

"The more Mom tried to keep me all to herself and treat me like a baby, the faster I grew up. Maybe because I was with grownups all the time. Anyway, I started running around when I was eleven.

"Mom worked. I had kids in after school. I cleaned the house, she never knew. Don't get me wrong. I didn't sleep around." She looked so mature when she said that. "People think teenagers are bed-hoppers, but not all of us, take it from me. But it sure is weird. You want to do things—crazy things—but something stops you. Maybe Mom has influenced me after all. Us kids, we go to movies, watch TV, especially soap operas. Boy, do you get ideas from there."

"What do you mean exactly?"

She look at me as if I was not for real. "Oh, you know, some guy who has a twenty-year-old daughter marries a girl her age or younger—a teenager like—stuff like that. Or a guy who is real rich, marries, has a son, then sets up housekeeping with a student nurse—like buys her a house and all that. You get ideas, know what I mean? Like, if they can do it, why not me? Why not some older rich guy?"

"Is that your plan?"

"To be honest, I don't know what my plan is. I'm still at school. I have a long way to go. But I know I'm not bad looking." She looked embarrassed. "It's OK for you to feel that you are nice to look at."

"You are, you know," I said encouragingly.

"Well, yah, I know but that's not everything. It kinda confuses you. My Mom treats me like a kid. Then the movies and TV, they show kids like me making love right there in front of you. You kinda get confused. Know what I mean?"

She was obviously having difficulty expressing herself.

"I guess I've talked too much. Shannon, she has a lot to learn."

"Hey, Judy, we'll be late for school. Can we come to see you again?"

"Sure, just phone ahead of time."

"Will do."

And they were gone.

About fifty percent of our thirteen to nineteen-year-olds are sexually active. Each year, one in ten teenage girls gets pregnant. These two statistics show us the strange combination of sophistication and naiveté that rests at the heart of the problem of teenage sexuality and parenting. Teenagers today are more familiar with sex, have more sex partners, and start taking part in sexual activities earlier than their parents' or grandparents' generations. Yet they are little better informed about contraception than previous generations.

Ironically, both elements have much to do with the media: While movies, films, and popular songs deal frankly with the sexual experience, teenagers often receive little or no information on how to prepare themselves for this experience. What information they do get often comes too late, or only through the diligent effort by the teenager to surmount the obstacles that society puts in the way of receiving this information.

Information quickly received and acted upon is basic to this generation's education. Bombarded with news, ads, and images on TV and used to instantaneous answers from computers and data banks, young people are ill-prepared to search for information that adults do not want them to have.

Television and the movies are our teenagers' models for real life. And the sad irony is that perhaps the only thing you do not learn from TV is birth control.

2
HOW COULD I TELL YOU?

She had been having pains all day. Cramps. They would last a while and then go away. She had become used to the pain the last four or five months.

The scream that brought her mother running was a combination of a dream and the stabbing pain through her back and abdomen.

Leila lay there doubled up, gritting her teeth, trying not to make any noise. Perspiration poured from her, her face contorted. Thankfully, the pain subsided. She looked at her mother desperately trying to say what she had to say but unable to do so. Her mother knelt down and tenderly wiped her face.

"What is it?" Again that question. The next pain grabbed her with such force that she again let out a scream which she tried desperately to suppress. Her whole body heaved and trembled.

"Leila, you're not—you can't be—how can you be?"

Eyes full of terror, face contorted with pain, sudden unbidden tears, so long held back, burst from Leila's eyes running every which way—on the pillow, into her half-opened mouth. She tasted salt.

Quickly, deftly her mother got her up, helped her dress, got dressed herself and in a matter of minutes, they were in the hospital.

Leila delivered a baby daughter five hours later. The whole thing was a blur of pain, nurses urging her to breathe a certain way, her mother holding her hands, encouraging her with loving words to do what she was told.

She didn't understand their words; she could only remember endless pain, people, nurses, doctors, just pushing, pulling, doing things to her— she was a thing—she couldn't think—she just let things happen to her. Through it all her mother, always there, kept her going with her quick, firm but loving hands, touching, holding, helping.

21

When she awoke, she was strangely at peace. She opened her eyes slowly, looked around; at first, for a few seconds not knowing, not remembering, just feeling great, at peace at last. Then she saw her mother dozing in a chair by her side.

Everything, but everything came back. That sense of peace, of well-being was shattered. Her heart beat faster, her body started to shake uncontrollably, her teeth chattering.

Oh God, what did I do? Why did I hurt her so?

Then tears, silent and sobbing. They went on for what seemed to be hours but were actually minutes. She lay back weak and spent. Slowly a decision formed from fear and despair. She set her mouth tight and lay there waiting tensely.

Suddenly the door opened and a cheery voice sang out, "Wake up, sleepy-head, time to see your baby."

Leila froze with fear. No, no, she won't! She turned her head away from the nurse, refusing to look at the baby.

"I'll take her."

She heard the calm, cool, controlled voice of her mother.

"Leila, wouldn't you like to see your daughter?"

"No!" came from the averted face and clenched teeth.

"Come on, dear, she's so little, she needs you, you worked so hard to bring her into the world."

Silence. She lay there not moving, hardly breathing.

"She's yours, you know, all yours, whether you like it or not."

"No, I won't," came the anguished cry from the bed.

She stayed in the hospital longer than others who had babies because of complications. Mother took the baby home, but continued to visit frequently, as did her Dad when he returned home from his business trip.

When she finally came home she was weak and was barely able to sit at the table for a meal. She stayed in her room and refused to talk. She went back to her summer job which later turned into a full-time job.

Leila finally relented and started to help with the baby after work. Patricia, as she was christened, was moved into her bedroom and she looked after her during the night.

What she felt inside no one knew.

Leila's mother phoned early one morning for an appointment.

"It's a bizarre situation. I'm baffled, upset and very, very guilty, all at once. No doubt you might have come across a situation like this, but I've always prided myself in being such an intelligent mother, an observant person. I can't believe it happened."

She fought back tears.

"I—you see—it's just that I never thought of Leila being involved in anything but school and music—a very active, accomplished young lady. No boys, absolutely no boys—and no running around, and no staying out late at night.

"To think what she went through—all by herself—a lonely, frightened child. How could I not see?

"You see," she was more composed, "my daughter, Leila, had a baby. I didn't know she was pregnant until she went into labor. It was horrible, horrible. She has a lovely baby girl, but she refuses to talk, I mean Leila does. She just goes through the day like a robot—working, home, and in her room. I can't bear it, to see her suffer, unable to share whatever is bothering her. Her father, well, he's beside himself with anxiety and anger at whoever did this.

"If it wouldn't be an imposition, if you would come over to the house some evening, maybe—I don't know—she might open up to you."

When I arrived both parents looked drawn and anxious. We spent two hours on small talk with Leila sitting quietly, listening. Not a word—just a pale, silent girl—sitting as if she was alone in the room. But she never took her eyes from me.

The next week I had a phone call from Leila. Her voice was low and pleasant but strained.

"This is Leila—you remember—you were at our house last week. . . .

"Is it possible—can I come—that is, in secret, sort of . . .," the little girl in her was showing, "I mean—I don't want my parents to know—they saw you and I don't want. . . ."

Leila—the silent watcher.

"Look, Leila, I can assure you that if you request that your parents not be involved. . . ."

"I don't want them to know ever what I tell you."

"That is your decision."

She seemed satisfied.

Her closed look was uncanny in one so young. She tossed back her long black hair, her pale face was drawn, her mouth set, her blue eyes were like ice. She was a tall girl but thinnish—her clothes hung on her.

"You must think I'm weird, the way I sat staring at you that time at the house—"

"No, not weird, but I did wonder—whether you were sort of sizing me up."

She looked startled and her face became suffused with red.

"Well, in a way. I checked you out . . .," again embarrassed, "I mean, I asked around—you know."

"Why don't you just relax and tell me whatever you feel like telling me."

She seemed a little relieved.

"OK. Well, Mom and Dad—I love them very much—they are great people. Well, they don't deserve what they are getting, but I couldn't help it. I don't know where to begin."

She stopped looking helplessly at me.

"OK, here goes! I'm seventeen. I finished high school last year. I studied hard, was into music, like singing and I'm a pretty good violinist. Being an only child, my parents gave me everything, that is, they encouraged me without pushing. You met them. They are terrific."

She took a deep breath and went on.

"I belonged to our church young peoples' group—I sang in the choir. I also organized a string quartet—I played the violin—classical mostly. We had fun, and I had lots of friends. No funny stuff."

Again a deep breath, or was it a sigh?

"Then Peter came. He had been away to school somewhere. He was older than most of us—but real nice.

"We—Peter and I—we became friends right away. You wouldn't believe this, you only saw me when I'm like this, but before I was lots of fun. I read a lot, we always talked about things at home, anyway, we hit it off. He was on holidays so he was around for two weeks. Actually we only made love twice. The first time, it just happened. It scared me. He was very apologetic. The second time, well, my folks were out and he brought me home from a party and, well, it happened again. We both felt guilty and, well, it happened. He left after the New Year. Mom and Dad never met him. I didn't want them to know—he was my secret, sort of, you know what I mean?"

She seemed to come alive when she talked about him. Her face flushed, her eyes bright, she looked beautiful.

"Anyway, he left. He said he would write and tell me where he was going to be. But he never did. When I missed the first period, I never thought anything of it. When my second period didn't come, well, I knew. I went on a strict diet. Waited and prayed. It never even entered my head

24

that he wouldn't write. Then I found out why by sheer accident. We were in a crowd—Peter's brother was there—someone said, 'Hey, how's Peter surviving the seminary?'

"I felt faint. From that day on, I lived in a fog—I just went through the days, weeks, months in a stupor. All I could think was to keep my parents from knowing. How could I tell them that the father was a priest, well, almost. I don't want them ever to know, ever!"

This came out in a painful sob. She cried quietly, just sat and cried without a sound. She blew her nose and looked at me with a faint smile.

"Believe it or not, I feel better. Like confession. You can be my priest," she smiled almost brightly.

"I'm flattered. But don't you think that you have to make some plans for yourself, your daughter?"

"Yes, of course, I do. Can I come back and talk—I mean, you're not too busy to see me?"

"No, I'll make time."

Leila was a joy to work with at all times. She ultimately went to university, continued with her music and became a teacher. Patricia was a lovely child, raised by Leila and her mother together.

Leila got married when Patricia was seven years old. Her husband adopted Patricia, and considered her his child. About a year later, Leila gave birth to a son. She named him Peter.

Most parents are bewildered by the sudden change that comes over their sons and daughters when they enter puberty.

Not so long ago they took pride in the fact that their offspring had been pretty good kids. They went on outings as a family, the children did errands when requested and generally seemed to be normal, often delightful companions.

Suddenly, at least it seemed that way to the parents, these nice, polite, well-behaved children became morose, irritable, stubborn, secretive, and unmanageable.

Mary is going to a party Friday evening. All the kids in her class are going too. Mother, as usual, drives her to the house where the party is being held and tells Mary that she will pick her up at ten p.m. Mary argues that it's too early but mother is adamant. "After all, you are only thirteen years old and should be home at a decent time."

At ten p.m. the party is in full swing and mother arrives. There is not an adult in sight and some couples are sitting very close in dark corners while others are dancing. The music is deafening. Mary is mortified at the sight of her mother.

"Mother, do I have to go home? I'm just starting to have fun."

Mother is not moved by her pleas. She takes in the situation and is appalled.

Mary grabs her coat, gets into the car, bangs the door, and bursts into tears.

"Oh mother, you made me feel like a baby, all the kids stay until two a.m. except me—they must think I'm sort of simple!"

When they get home Mary runs into the house, up to her room and throws herself on the bed crying hysterically. Mother walks downstairs, upset, puzzled, and feeling a little helpless. She talks to her husband. As usual he leaves that sort of thing to her. "She'll be OK, she'll get over it," he assures her.

This was the beginning of a battle between mother and daughter, sometimes erupting like a volcano. Mary would stay out longer than permitted and would then be grounded. She began to stay out until all hours of the morning. Her marks and attendance at school dropped drastically.

The guerilla warfare was in full swing, with mother losing ground steadily. The bewildered parents kept asking each other where they went wrong.

When teenagers come from a family where there is a loving relationship, where there are firm but fair guidelines, where there is a continuity and consistency on the part of the parents in the manner which they interact with the teenager, by and large, the teenager will cope much better with the stormy years ahead.

We let the kids have their say. We don't encroach on their privacy. We can't be with them all the time, so we have to trust them. But we stress that we will stand by them when they need us.

When parents are open and are prepared to listen to reasonable explanations and respect each other as well as the teenager, the prognosis is good for all concerned.

When there is recognition on the part of the parents that there are many forces out there beguiling their young sons and daughters, and when an effort is made to deal with them, then the future looks brighter.

Keeping lines of communication open pays off. Parents are the adults. They have to be sensitive to the changing moods and recognize the stirring of strange new sensations that every adolescent during puberty experiences. Every teenager experiences many pressures and expectations from his or her peers, teachers, and parents. They are expected not only to participate but excel in sports and their studies and at the same time be polite, amiable, and amenable.

That does not mean that expectations should not be high, that parents should not have high standards of integrity, honesty, respect for others, and recognition of other peoples' needs. Nor does it mean that we should not inculcate all these values as guidelines in interpersonal relations.

What Can Parents Do?

It is generally agreed that most children learn by osmosis. It is not what parents *say*, it is what they *do* that is important. Parents cannot boast about how the accountant has cheated on their income tax return and at the same time lecture their children on the virtues of honesty, integrity, decency, and regard for others. They know when we are trying to beat the system. Children are not stupid nor deaf and dumb. They listen, hear, and absorb. We, as parents, are their models. So we cannot entirely ignore our responsibility for their behavior.

Tragically, too many parents are so absorbed in their own personal problems and unmet needs that they are unable to cope with their own lives. The pre-teen and teenager left to his/her own devices looks elsewhere for acceptance, for affection, and for some gratification of deep-seated emotional needs.

As parents, we can love, guide, understand, set standards, be consistent and sensitive to a child who is bewildered, upset, unhappy and be prepared to stand by them when they need it most urgently.

Part of the problem with so many parents is that we refuse to accept the fact that our children suddenly grow up to be adolescents and finally adults. We want to hang onto them and pretend that they are still children.

Indeed they still have many of the emotional needs of children, but they have other needs, too. They are confused and upset with their new feelings and new bodies.

Our job is to understand and lovingly guide them through the stormy years ahead. Instead we give them double signals. We pretend they are still children and yet tell them not to get pregnant. That is the extent of sex information given by many parents to their young daughters.

27

What are we saying? Have sex but don't get pregnant? No wonder kids are confused.

When teenagers become sexually involved, they become very secretive, fearful of letting their parents know. The responsible ones who go to a doctor or clinic to obtain birth control aids have mothers rifling through their drawers, finding the birth control pills, and throwing them down the drain.

Such parents berate the daughter, the doctor, and/or the clinic personnel, blaming them for contributing to juvenile delinquency. Then they wonder why the daughter becomes pregnant.

"I'm worried about my daughter, so many of her friends are pregnant. How can I prevent her from being in the same position?"

"How old is she?" I asked.

"She's fifteen, but she's well developed for her age."

"Have you talked to her about protection?"

"You mean birth control?"

"Yes."

"Of course not. If I did she might think that she can go ahead—you know, that I was encouraging her. I have warned her not to sleep around and get pregnant, but I can't be with her all the time."

Most parents find themselves in this bind. They worry about pregnancy, but to discuss birth control is both against their concept of morality and at the same time they are fearful of being misunderstood. Besides, many parents are embarrassed or self-conscious and often not knowledgeable in this area.

This means that teenagers are on their own. In order to get the information they need, they must go outside the family and seek professional guidance. Yet, even when they behave more responsibly than their parents, they are often thwarted by the very people who should be helping them, as we shall see in the next chapter.

3
TRUST ME

"Well, you are indeed pregnant, about ten weeks I'd say."

Her heart started to beat wildly, but she had to ask him.

"Could I—would it be possible—I mean—I'd like an abortion." She blurted this out breathlessly. She could see him visibly stiffening, his eyes becoming like two burning coals, boring into her.

"Sorry, young lady, I don't do that sort of thing. Call Pregnancy Distress. They are very good people—they will help you."

She breathed a sigh of relief and thanked him profusely.

She was neatly dressed, her hair dull brown and straggly. Her skin caught my attention—it was blotched—dark patches and the rest of it was gray. She had large, dark brown eyes which were staring as if in shock. It was the shape of her body that startled me. With her thin arms, slender body, and protruding stomach, she looked like a misshapen child. She sensed my surprise.

"Yes, I'm gonna have a baby I didn't and don't want."

She looked so young! My heart went out to her. She was, I guessed, maybe fifteen.

"I read this here article. You said girls can choose, I mean if they want an abortion—"

"Well, I didn't quite mean—or rather not at your stage." Now I was groping for words.

She looked at me, not quite understanding my confusion. "No, oh no, I don't mean—I know it's too late for me, like I'm gonna have the baby anyway. But I want to know something—will you tell me, if I asked something important?"

"I'll try—no promises ahead of time."

29

"I wanna know if, when I got pregnant, like in the second or maybe third month, could I have—you know—maybe had an abortion?"

I hesitated.

"Please, please, I wanna know—it's important."

"Well, usually, when the girls come early enough we have them see the doctor." I was letting her down. She wanted something from me and I was not giving it.

"Listen, why don't you tell me what is bothering you—I'd like to help if I can."

"Please, please, tell me . . .," she continued to plead.

"Just relax, I'll try and tell you what I can."

Her taut, straining body, leaning out of the chair, crumbled. Her sobs came in big gasps, as if struggling for air. I was by her side, holding her, trying to soothe.

"Me and my boyfriend, he's seventeen and very nice and we decided that I should have an abortion. We talked and talked—and the doctor said to go to Pregnancy Distress. So we did. My Mom and Dad didn't know anything about, you know. . . . It was only my second month." She sat quietly for awhile, her hands circling the coffee mug, leaning against the desk, as if for support.

"It was horrible, those great big pictures of fet . . . like when the baby starts to grow—it looks like a fish—" She stopped and shivered. "They kept saying that we would be killers and that we would be sorry for the rest of our lives that we killed our own flesh and blood. We were so scared. They gave my boyfriend hell—they said he was more to blame than me, 'cause well, we shoulda waited until we were married. They said the baby would be taken by a real nice couple—y'know what I mean—they said abortion was wicked and that I couldn't get one anyhow."

"Are you sure they said that?"

"Oh, yes," she started to cry again.

I held her, as her tears started to flow again.

"I'm sorry."

"Well, yah, that's what I wanted to tell you. I guess I'd better go. My boyfriend—he's waiting in the car."

"Are you putting the baby up for adoption?"

"Yah, I guess so. I wanna finish grade twelve and go into nursing. Do you think they'll accept me—would they have to know?"

"I doubt if you will have any trouble—how are your marks?"

"Pretty good," she answered listlessly, "Mostly A's."

"Really—aren't you rather young to be in grade twelve?"
"Maybe—sort of—I'll be seventeen in a couple of months."
She looked about fourteen to me.
"Will you let me know when you have your baby?"
"Yah, I guess so, if you like."
"If there is anything I can do to help, please call me."
For the first time since she arrived—her whole face lit up—she looked pretty, animated.
"Can I?" She walked slowly to the door, turned and said, looking wistfully around her, "I wish . . . If I had known . . . before."

Doctors are people, too. They have prejudices, attitudes, values and they bring them all to their practice of medicine. They, too, are products of a certain upbringing and are influenced by the same forces that influence us.

Many doctors are associated with various religions and/or pro-life groups which lobby against abortions, birth control, and pre-marital sex. The Canadian Medical Association passed a resolution at their meeting in June, 1978, that states: ". . . an ethical physician . . . when his morality or religious conscience alone prevents him from recommending some form of therapy, will so acquaint the patient."

The resolution then went on to say that the doctor did not have to send the person to another doctor who did not have the same moral conviction.

As a result, many young girls either get a lecture on morality and are sent away, or their parents are notified.

So, how can a teenage girl find a sympathetic doctor to give her birth control information and aids? How can she find a gynecologist or counselor who will help her early in her pregnancy?

First, do not go to your mother's doctor, especially if he is a personal friend of the family unless you want her to know that you are sexually active, but are afraid to tell her.

Second, do not pick a name from the telephone book.

Sometimes a knowledgeable friend can help, one who has had personal experience with such a doctor or who knew one through her friends. Sometimes a boyfriend knows about "friendly" doctors from his friends.

Phone a nurse who assists a gynecologist (women's specialist), or if under sixteen, a pediatrician is OK too, especially the younger ones. They are often more in touch with the current situation than their older colleagues.

At a recent meeting of the Canadian Medical Association, this issue was discussed by concerned doctors. It was recommended that more attention be paid to helping teenagers prevent unwanted pregnancies. They advised that younger doctors be encouraged to be up-to-date in birth control methods, as younger doctors may be more amenable to help such youngsters than older doctors.

If you go to a clinic, say that you prefer a younger doctor since you are young yourself. That, of course, doesn't always work, but it's worth a try.

One way to find out how a doctor might treat you is to call his nurse and ask her if the doctor accepts teenage patients who are seeking birth control aids. She will tell you one way or another. If she hesitates or starts to ask too many questions, politely thank her for her interest and hang up. If not, give her your age—that usually gets some reaction. Remember you have nothing to lose. She doesn't know who you are. You have a right to "shop around."

Many girls prefer women doctors in the naive belief that they are more sympathetic than men. This is not necessarily true. Women doctors have their own hangups, the same as men. Many women, especially those who have graduated in the past ten years, can be and usually are sympathetic. But do not take it for granted that they *all* are. I have seen any number of tearful girls who had gone to women doctors and were given a rough time.

Your best bet is to call Planned Parenthood. Many branches in the U.S. run birth control clinics. In Canada, they do not, but they no doubt would steer you to a doctor who is willing to treat you sympathetically.

You could also go to a community or private clinic. Usually, these are listed under Physicians and Surgeons in the phone book. If the various services are listed and Family Planning is highlighted, chances are a teenager would be welcome. If you phone an organization other than Planned Parenthood, check it out carefully. Be careful about names like "Pregnancy Distress" which is a pro-life group. If the clinic offers pregnancy counseling, ask if abortions are performed. Remember they don't know who you are. You are just a voice on the other end of the telephone line. Do not settle for anything less than a straight answer. If they won't give you one, try elsewhere.

4
WHO CAN I ASK?

"Our teacher assigned a project—two of us are supposed to do it."

"What is the name of your project?"

"Various methods of birth control and how some work and some don't."

"How can I help you?"

We usually get about two or three a week. The teachers are trying to get the girls to get the information themselves. A good method.

"Well," the young voice was hesitant. "We have these here pamphlets and your book *Pregnant and Alone*, can we kinda talk to you about that?"

The anxiety in her voice was becoming evident over the phone.

They came the next day. Grade twelve students, notebooks in hand, ready to begin.

"There are a few methods we don't quite understand."

The speaker was a short, dark, chubby girl with lively black eyes and an olive skin with a bird-like, fast-nodding face.

"We don't see, I mean, why do you say that you can get pregnant if you use coi. . . ." She frantically searched for the right page.

"You mean *coitus interruptus* or the withdrawal method?"

"Yes."

There was a quick exchange of looks between her and the other girl—blonde, quiet, a little on the pale side.

"What don't you understand?"

"We understand, it's just we disagree with you." She looked ill at ease.

"That is your privilege. But anyone anxious *not* to get pregnant, is

33

taking a chance in using this method. In the first place, the guys are young, not too experienced and sometimes don't get out in time."

Again they exchanged glances.

"Then there is the possibility of a drop emerging from the penis which has about 300,000 sperm, enough to impregnate a girl 300 times."

"Hasn't it ever worked?" The anxiety in her voice was intense.

"Sometimes. But unless girls want to take a chance, I wouldn't advise it."

"Why do you dismiss the rhythm method as no good?"

"Well, I explained it in my book. You said you read it."

"Yes, but we disagree."

"On what grounds?"

"Well, we just think you're wrong."

Some parents can discuss every phase of human development with their children effectively. Those teenagers—and their parents—are lucky. They have no doubt given the children a survival kit containing values which will help them get over the turbulent years and cope effectively with life.

Another dilemma!

Many mothers are open and do discuss birth control with their daughters. But their daughters refuse to share confidences of an activity which they consider private. Teenagers of such mothers claim that they are still being treated like kids when asked to go with their mother to her doctor. In addition, that would be admitting that she is sexually active, and the majority of teenagers don't want to admit this to their parents.

Other parents wait for the daughter to ask questions, which they hope they will not be too embarrassed to answer. Many children, both sons and daughters, do not ask questions. They have picked up all sorts of information from their friends, and never question whether it is accurate or not.

At a recent lecture I gave to students at a university on the topic "Sex and the Teenager," about ninety percent of the audience readily admitted that they learned about sex from TV, their peers, and books, in that order. What they learned was often inaccurate and misleading. Only ten percent (girls) received some information from their mothers.

Yet, there are many books and pamphlets prepared by knowledgeable professionals available through the health departments in every city and town. There are literally thousands of clinics which cater to young people, male or female. If only parents would recognize that giving information about human sexuality and how to prevent pregnancy is not an invitation to partake. Experience has taught us that those kids who do get caught are uninformed and misinformed and are forced to swim in troubled waters without having had a swimming lesson.

How much easier it would be if parents would once and for all face the reality of the 1980s and encourage the teaching of human sexuality in the schools, the same as biology and history are taught.

Knowledge does not mean instant use. When a road is dangerous a sign is put up to warn drivers. The sign is a warning not an invitation.

Teenagers are hungry for authoritative knowledge about their own bodies and those of the opposite sex. As a first step to setting the record straight, here is a short description of basic birth control methods and their effectiveness. But, before we can properly understand contraception, we must understand conception and the menstrual cycle.

The menstrual cycle is a chemically activated process. Four hormones are activated by the pituitary gland which is found at the base of the brain. They are produced in a particular order and at particular times of the month.

Around the time of the menstrual period, the blood stream is very low in hormones. The pituitary gland receives a message that estrogen and progesterone are needed to prepare the uterus for the next cycle. The pituitary gland produces a hormone called Follicle Stimulating Hormone

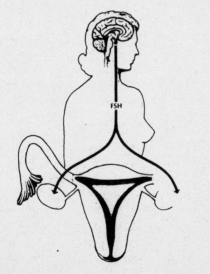

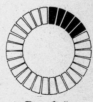

Menstrual Cycle

Days 1–5

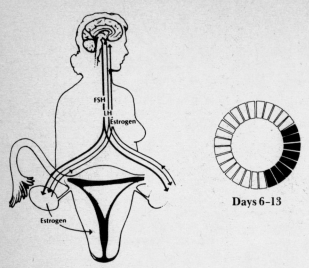

Days 6-13

(FSH), which travels to one of the ovaries. The ovary contains tens of thousands of eggs contained in sacs or follicles. When the FSH arrives at the ovary, it stimulates one follicle to produce estrogen. At this stage, the FSH has completed its work, and is no longer secreted during that cycle.

A second hormone now begins to work. Lutenizing Hormone (LH) is

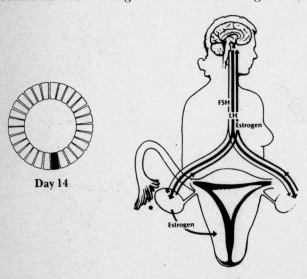

Day 14

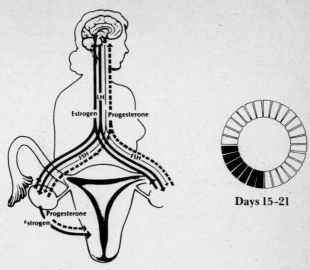

Days 15–21

now produced by the pituitary gland to help the follicle release the egg, which is "ripe" to receive a sperm. The egg moves from the follicle to the Fallopian tubes, where it stays for two to four days. During this time, the follicle is still producing estrogen, but now it begins to produce another hormone, progesterone, as well. Progesterone helps the estrogen thicken

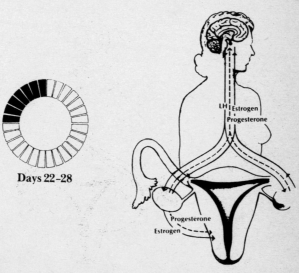

Days 22–28

37

the ovary wall and also provides a rich source of nutrients for the fertilized egg. In this way, the egg can develop into a fetus.

If there is no fertilized egg to settle in the uterus (i.e. conception does not take place) the process slows down, the thick lining of the uterus begins to shed, and what we know as menstruation begins.

Although the process is the same in every woman, the duration of the parts of the cycle differs. Therefore it is very difficult to know exactly when the ripened egg is in the Fallopian tubes ready to receive the sperm. It is just as difficult to predict a woman's "safe" days, the days when she will not get pregnant if intercourse occurs. As a woman goes through the process of producing eggs and preparing her body for pregnancy every month for about thirty years, the risk of encountering an "unsafe" time must be faced again and again. This is why it is very difficult to avoid pregnancy without an effective form of birth control device.

5

A GUIDE TO BIRTH CONTROL

For centuries, men and women have attempted to control conception. Some methods of birth control are very old, and have changed little over the years. Others are more recent developments, resulting from scientists' increasing understanding of the biological processes of conception and birth.

Birth control methods vary in effectiveness. Some rely on physical or mechanical interference in the conception process; others rely on interrupting the chemical balance needed for conception to take place.

We will begin our discussion with one of the oldest (and least effective) methods and end with the most effective, modern methods.

The age-old form of birth control called *coitus interruptus* or *withdrawal* is based on a simple premise: if no sperm reach the vagina, the woman will not become pregnant. This is a fine premise in theory, but it is very difficult, if not impossible, to put into practice. Before ejaculation, the man must withdraw the penis from the vagina so that no fluid can swim up into the uterus and fertilize the egg. However, this method is rarely effective. Even prior to ejaculation any number of drops of fluid may enter the vagina. Each drop can contain as many as 300,000 sperm, any one of which can cause pregnancy.

There is a further problem with the withdrawal method: it is often difficult to know exactly when ejaculation will occur, and often the penis cannot be removed from the vagina in time. At the time of ejaculation, the penis must be well away from the lips of the vagina, as sperm deposited externally can swim through lubricant and into the uterus. As you can see,

39

there are many risks with this method, and it is not recommended if pregnancy must be avoided.

A second traditional form of birth control is the *rhythm method*. This method depends on the premise that there is a time, during a woman's menstrual cycle, when sexual intercourse will not cause pregnancy; this "safe period" is the time of ovulation, before the egg is formed and sent down the Fallopian tubes. This "safe" period will last about ten days, including the days of menstruation.

Ovulation may be predicted in two ways. Some doctors believe that a woman's body temperature rises about 1°F during this time of her cycle; therefore, by paying close attention to her body temperature, a woman can discover when she is ovulating. The second way of monitoring the time of ovulation is by recording when menstrual periods begin.

In either case—daily temperature checks or monthly recording of periods—many months must be monitored before a woman can be relatively sure of her cycle. The time of ovulation will vary among women; moreover, a woman's cycle may vary from month to month. The problem, therefore, is to determine a woman's "rhythm," which may be irregular and can be easily upset by physical or emotional factors. Obviously, this is not a reliable method for most women.

Related to the withdrawal method is the *condom* or *safe*, which keeps the sperm from entering the vagina. The condom is a rubber sheath, which covers the penis during intercourse. Ideally, no sperm will escape the sheath, and pregnancy will be avoided. However, there are problems with this seemingly simple procedure. The most obvious is the possibility that the sheath will break, or that it may have a tiny tear or hole in it. Another problem is that the condom should be fitted *before* intercourse begins, as sperm may be present before ejaculation. Finally, the sheath must be held in place during withdrawal; otherwise, its contents may spill into the vagina.

When used properly, the condom is about seventy percent effective as a birth control device, and an excellent protection against venereal disease. It does, however, put the responsibility for birth control on the male partner, unless used in conjunction with a spermicidal foam, cream, or gel.

Vaginal spermicides are chemical substances that kill sperm, yet do not harm the delicate tissue of the vagina or penis. Before intercourse, a pre-measured amount of the foam or gel is inserted into the vagina by means of an applicator.

When the man uses a condom and the woman uses a spermicidal foam or gel, they are ninety percent protected.

Another mechanical means of birth control is the *diaphragm*. This is a round rubber cap with a springy rim, which covers the cervix, the entrance to the uterus. It remains in place for at least six hours after intercourse, and thus prevents the sperm from entering the uterus. The diaphragm must be the proper size to be effective; as well, it must be inserted properly so that the cervix is completely covered. The fitting and initial insertion of the diaphragm should be done by a doctor. He or she will also explain how it should be used.

The diaphragm must be cared for: it should be checked frequently for holes or tears, and must be washed after each use. If used properly, in conjunction with a spermicidal gel, the diaphragm is a relatively effective method of birth control.

A more effective method is the *intrauterine device*. This is the modern form of a very ancient type of device. Centuries ago, a foreign object—often a sea sponge or gold ring—was introduced into the vagina in order to inhibit conception. The intrauterine device or IUD uses this principle in conjunction with scientific discoveries of safe materials and effective shapes. The IUD is inserted by a physician and remains in the uterus for up to two years. The physician will then remove or replace it. The IUD is one of the most convenient birth control devices and can be used by most women. However, there may be some initial discomfort when the device is inserted, and it may increase menstrual cramps. These side-effects are not usually serious, and the IUD is ninety-three–ninety-seven percent effective.

The most modern, and most effective, non-permanent birth control device is the *oral contraceptive* or *"the pill,"* which was developed after scientists began to understand how a woman's hormones work. The pill contains two hormones: estrogen and progesterone. The estrogen inhibits the egg development; the progesterone causes the uterus lining to be less receptive to the sperm. Also, it causes a thick layer of mucus to form over the cervix, thus preventing any sperm from entering the uterus.

The pill is not recommended for all women: those with poor blood circulation, hepatitis, or cystic fibrosis should not use it. Some other women may have minor side-effects such as headaches, increase in weight, and cramps in their legs. Research is continuing into possible side-effects of the pill, but no serious side-effects have been proven as yet. The pill is virtually one hundred percent effective in preventing pregnancies.

The Diaphragm

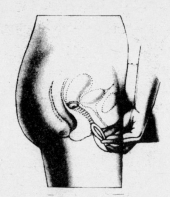

Insertion

Placement

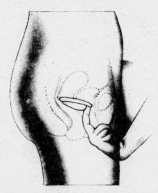

Removal

The IUD

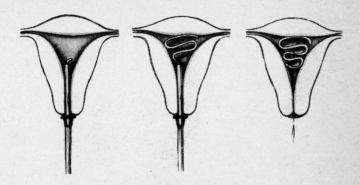

Insertion and Placement of Lippes Loop

The only method more effective than the pill is *sterilization* of either the male or female partner. When a man has a *vasectomy*, the doctor makes a small cut in the scrotum (usually under a local anesthetic), and cuts the two vas deferens, the tubes that carry the sperm from the testes to the penis. As sperm produced before the operation may be in the ejaculate up to three months after the operation, another form of birth control must be used during this period. However, after the three months, the sterilization should be complete, and usually irreversible.

When a woman has a *tubal ligation*, the Fallopian tubes are cut and tied off, so that the egg cannot get to the uterus. This is a major operation, and must be performed in a hospital. (A vasectomy is considered a minor operation and can be performed in the doctor's office.)

Both the vasectomy and tubal ligation are permanent. Both prevent conception without interfering with hormone production or sexual function.

SECTION TWO

What Are My Options?

"What are you going to do?"
"Do?"
"Are you going to tell your parents?"
"Nope."
"What about when it starts to show? What are your plans?"
"Dunno."
"Well, you better start giving it some thought."
"Maybe I'm not really pregnant. Doctors can be wrong sometimes."

In Section One, we saw that the results of teenage sexuality too often lead to pregnancy through lack of information about birth control. This section discusses the options for a pregnant teenager.

Why do teenagers carry a child to term? The answers are as varied as the teenagers; but they fall into several broad categories. The first is a matter of principle, either the teenager's or her parents' if she is a minor: the belief that abortion is morally offensive or "the easy way out." The second is simple fear, refusing to acknowledge that the fetus is there or that there is only a limited time during which an abortion can take place. The third is simply wanting the child.

But whatever the reason, the fact remains that carrying to term can be dangerous, both for the mother and the child.

6

TWO STORIES ON PRINCIPLE

Lynda

A girl was staring at me, big brown eyes with long curly lashes. Her smile lighted her whole face which was strikingly beautiful.

I just couldn't put a name to her face.

Of course, it all came back in a flash after reading the skimpy notes I made. Seven years.

I remembered so well.

Then, as she did today, she sat waiting for the doctor. But then her boyfriend Jeff sat holding her hand. He was a giant of a young man about nineteen years old. Curly, sun-bleached blond hair, about six foot two to her five foot three. He was attending university and playing football.

She was pregnant; he wanted her to have an abortion. Very logical, very persuasive.

"Look, it's not like the usual kids you probably see here." He started off, then realizing what he had said, he backtracked quickly.

"I mean, I love her, we have each other. I'm going to marry her. It's just I want to finish my courses, go into law, and well, then we can be independent, I mean—I want to look after her." He seemed ill at ease suddenly. "We are too young. I mean, she is and so am I.

"We sort of grew up together. I've known her since she was twelve, and we were careful. It's just so crazy. I must have made a mistake or something. I guess it's because we were together a lot during the school

47

break. I guess it must have happened then." He looked at her for affirmation. She looked down, her cheeks burning.

"Are you OK, hon? I mean—you're not sick or anything?"

She continued to look down, cheeks blazing and shook her head negatively.

"Do you want to talk about this—what do you want to do?"

She looked quickly at him and in a hardly audible whisper said, "I don't know."

"Oh great, this is really something." His voice took on a note of impatience. "She needs a baby like a hole in the head. We both agreed that she should continue school. She was planning to go into education. She's a top student. Money is no problem, her old man is loaded."

Again, she seemed to grow smaller. I could sense her wincing.

"I don't see any other answers. I'm not ready for marriage, nor is she. We're too young. It would be crazy."

He moved his chair away from her. He was visibly angry.

"Before you go any further, I would like to suggest that you speak to your parents first," I spoke, a little too loudly.

"Her parents? What for?"

"Sorry, they are not *my* rules. In this city all hospitals demand that parents of a minor give written permission for an abortion—or for any surgical procedure for that matter. There is no other way."

He strode out ahead of her. She turned to me, "I'm sorry." Her eyes pleaded for understanding.

"He's not always like this. He's upset. He's really a sweet guy."

Lynda's mother phoned to make an appointment.

Do I mind if Jeff's parents came along—at least his mother was anxious to be involved.

They arrived a few minutes early and I noticed them at once in the waiting room. She was slender, dressed with good taste. He was tall and distinguished looking with steel blue eyes.

Jeff Wilson's mother was big with gray, unkempt hair. Florid face, chapped hands, fingernails broken. She seemed ill at ease and kept tugging at her coat which was too small for her.

Lynda's mother spoke with a low, melodious voice and precise English. A teacher?

"Thank you for seeing us at such short notice. We hope we have not put you out unduly." She stopped, looked at her husband. I waited.

"Lynda asked us to discuss this with you." Again a pause while looking at her husband.

His voice was deep. "I hope you don't mind if we come to the point." He was uncomfortable.

"We are somewhat out of our depth. Lynda is our youngest, the others are married and settled. We are disappointed," his voice almost broke. Suddenly he looked as if he was about to cry. His wife stirred in her chair and put her hand on his arm.

Suddenly I felt sorry for him, for her, and for Jeff's mother, who sat on the edge of her chair, perspiring profusely, her anxious eyes darting back and forth.

"It's Jeff's fault—I wish I could do something." Mrs. Wilson's hands clutched the big purse on her lap. She looked uneasy.

"Lynda told us she was pregnant and that we were to see you. We were stunned at first. Then we decided to suggest alternatives, but she refused to talk about anything."

"What alternatives did you have in mind?"

"Well, if she wants to get married, we have an extra small house on our property, she can live rent-free there and Jeff can continue with his studies . . . ."

Jeff's mother interrupted, "That's very generous, I mean about not having to quit school. But he's mad, and won't talk to us—I mean to me."

"What other alternatives did you offer?" I was curious.

"What else is there? We don't relish the thought of her going through with an abortion."

"Are you against abortions?"

She began. "You might as well know, I'm unalterably opposed to abortion, it is murder."

He looked stern, forbidding. "Jeff . . . he . . . well I cannot forgive what he did to her."

The air was heavy with suppressed anger. Mrs. Wilson stirred, looking anxiously and pleadingly at Lynda's father.

"Please don't misunderstand. It's just when you are brought up a certain way and try to bring your children up the same way, well, it's hard to swallow when one of them, well, strays." She finished in a breathless whisper.

They thanked me politely and left.

I was beginning to understand Lynda's dilemma.

She arrived the next day without an appointment. She was pale and her eyes were red.

"I feel as if I'm imposing on you, first my parents, then me. I love and respect them, and I don't want to hurt them, but I guess it's too late for that. Jeff is very unhappy. We both feel trapped. I want to marry him, but not now. Still, an abortion—"

She wept quietly, wiping the tears away as quickly as they came.

"Jeff is so angry—he's frustrated. He likes to make his own decisions."

She sat up and said very quickly, as if betraying a trust, "My Dad and Jeff don't get along too well. They argue about everything, religion, politics, and now, well, Jeff hates the thought of being in his power, well, dependent, you understand, don't you?"

Yes, I understood all right. She was an intelligent kid. The situation was untenable and I was helpless.

"Look, it's not the end of the world. You can go back to school and continue your education."

She looked at me sadly. Her face was drawn and she looked older.

"No, I'll never go back to school. I'll get a job and help support Jeff. He'll feel better if the money came from me rather than from my Dad."

She got up slowly, hesitated as if wanting to say something, but decided against it. "Thank you. I'm sorry we were such a bother."

She nodded and left. Seven years ago.

"So you are back after all this time?" I began.

She looked flustered. Out of character, I thought.

"It's just that it was more convenient to go to mother's gynecologist—I had the baby—a beautiful boy." Her face changed—pride, love shone from it.

"I tried, I really tried," she burst out. When the tears came, she was impatient with herself and angry.

"This is how you saw me the last time. What must you think?

"Why do parents force their value systems on their children? My parents have lived their lives, why couldn't they leave us alone?"

Once again my heart went out to her—she was so bitter.

"It's so hard for me to tell you. I love my parents and I love Jeff. We even had a proper church wedding, Catholic, of course.

"Well, Jeff just seemed to grow away from me. He resented the whole situation. So he buried himself in his studies. I wanted to work, but my parents wouldn't let me. I seemed to be in the middle always trying to keep the peace. Jeff is a lawyer now. He did well, top marks. But he's a stranger to me. I still love him, but he hasn't forgiven any of it. He feels cheated. And now its too late." The sadness in her voice cut like a knife.

"Surely, there must be something?" I was so sorry for her.

"No, I'm going to have an abortion."

"You what?" I couldn't help my reaction, remembering the first time her ambivalence.

"Oh, I've changed, and how I've changed. Jeff and I, we hadn't slept together for almost a year. We were strangers, polite strangers. So I went off the pill.

"Well, we were out, he had a few drinks, and I, well, I love him still, but I won't make the same mistake again. I won't tie him down with another child.

"He just wants to be free—free to go and do as he pleases and not be tied down. Actually, I understand him and his yearning for freedom. He has felt trapped for so long, that now that he can afford it, he wants out."

"How do you know? Did he tell you?" I tried again. "There must be something."

"He doesn't have to tell me, I just know."

She had the abortion. Again I did not hear from her.

About four years later, I noticed her picture in the paper. She had won a scholarship and a gold medal in psychology. She was leaving for university for her Masters degree.

Lynda's parents were devout Catholics, convinced that abortion is murder.

They loved their daughter, as she loved them. But nothing in their experience as parents prepared them for a decision which would affect their daughter for the rest of her life. It was an awesome responsibility.

Lynda was young and ambivalent. She wanted to please her parents, yet hoped they would decide on an abortion for her. At the same time, she loved Jeff and wanted to please him too.

Most importantly, being a minor she was legally unable to decide for herself. Sixteen is a tender age.

Jeff, of course, felt trapped and resentful, yet loved Lynda and wanted to marry her, but not under such circumstances. But the resentment grew like a cancer between them and ultimately destroyed their relationship. Both were too young, and they grew farther apart. As time elapsed, it became more difficult for either one to do something about their marriage.

Yet, when I first saw them, love shone from their eyes, and their bright, happy faces could have lit the room.

Gaylene

The tension in the room was palpable. Sixteen-year-old Gaylene was weeping silently. Her grim-faced, determined mother sat a little away from her not looking at her daughter.

Suddenly she snapped. "Stop sniveling. This time you will not get your own way."

"Please, Mom, please. I can't go through with this. I'm scared. I want—"

"You should have thought of that when you started messing around with Tim. I felt it in my bones that something was going on between the two of you."

"Mom, nothing went on. We just did it once, that's all."

"A likely story!" Mother said almost spitting out the words. "You were brought up in a God-fearing home. We tried to teach you right from wrong. What you did is wrong, Gaylene, and you are going to be punished. You can cry all you want."

"I promise I'll never do it again. I promise. But don't—"

"No it's too late. I warned you time and time again that no daughter of mine was going to have an abortion."

"But, I can't—my schooling, my piano. I'll be writing my finals," Gaylene tried again. "Please, Mom, help me."

Her mother turned to me grim-faced. "Look, I came because Gaylene asked me. But, I will not go against my profound belief that abortion is murder, pure and simple. Besides, she should be punished for going against everything her parents believe in. Kids think they can do what they want and when they get into trouble, somebody else will pick up the pieces.

"I will not allow her to have an abortion. That's final. We will arrange for her to go into a home for unwed mothers and the baby will be adopted. Thank you for your time."

Teenagers who face an unplanned pregnancy are beset by a multiplicity of problems for which they are hardly prepared. In most cases, fear takes over—fear of telling their parents, fear of going to a doctor, fear of the future. This precludes the ability to make rational long-range decisions. But their inactivity or lack of taking action, in itself, is a decision.

What is horrifying for young teenagers, sixteen or under, is their helplessness.

When parents feel strongly about abortions, pro or con, they can make a decision that has a lifelong effect on their daughter. Yet, the daughter has literally no say in the matter.

7

MOTHER WILL TAKE CARE OF EVERYTHING

"Me and my brothers, we're kinda fed up with Mom."

How well I knew that family. There were eight of them. Shirley, the mother had had her first child at sixteen. She kept having them yearly, one after another.

We tried to get her to use some form of birth control, but with her drinking problem, the only method that did not take her cooperation was the coil (IUD). But it always seemed to fall out, or maybe she pulled it out. Who knows?

"She's such a slob."

I looked at Vicky, astonished. She used to be very shy, yet hungry for affection. She would stretch out her arms whenever I walked into the Day Hospital and shyly crawl into mine, nestle against me and settle in for a visit. As she grew, she became more withdrawn, hiding behind the older children.

"She never cleans or anything—she just lies around all day, or takes off whenever she feels like it. Even for a whole weekend. Us kids, we sort of look after each other. But sometimes, like there is no food, no nuthin', y'know what I mean?"

How well I knew! It was always Friday when we dropped off the children—we always had three or four of them with all sorts of ailments. The house was always chaotic with broken furniture and garbage piled up everywhere, floors caked with dirt from months of neglect.

Friday was pay day, so her husband was not home. No milk, no food, no money.

If Shirley was sober, we would have our weekly talk and listen to promises and more promises—she knew that milk and bread would be left for her.

"Is she getting worse, I mean, is she drinking more than before?" I asked wondering, "Who is left of those eight, they must all be gone?"

"Me and the twins, we're used to her drinkin'. It's when she isn't drinking, she becomes nuts—"

"How do you mean 'nuts'?"

"Oh, she runs around making us stay home from school, clean the house, do her errands, y'know what I mean?"

"Doesn't that interfere with your school work?"

"Yah, it sure does—I'm gonna fail this year, I just know it."

"The Children's Aid—aren't they involved?" I was beginning to worry.

"Yah, sure, but we're kinda grown, like the twins are gonna be sixteen and me, I'm fourteen, well, fifteen soon. . . ."

"Vicky, your Mom has been like that for years, so—"

"I know, I know, it's just, I don't know what to do, like how will I bring up my baby?" She looked anxiously at me, her breath suspended.

How stupid of me. Of course she's pregnant. It was her way of introducing what was really troubling her.

She looked ill at ease, a little frightened. "The nurses, they said I should be on birth control pills. I didn't do nothing, so I didn't want them."

Logic!

"Does your mother know?" I was getting upset, knowing full well what would happen.

"No! That's just it, I don't know what she'll do. She gets so mad at nuthin'! Just screams, or throws things around, or even tears clothes—like she goes nuts—know what I mean?"

I nodded, waiting, hoping.

"Me and my boyfriend, he wants me to have an abortion—he says, like, maybe he won't be around like later, y'know what I mean?"

I nodded. She had an anxious, pinched look on her otherwise chubby, round face and her big, brown, slightly slanted eyes looked at me pleading for understanding.

"How do you feel about the pregnancy?"

"Me? I wanna go to school, maybe work in an office, but my Mom, she maybe would wanna have a baby. She can't have any more, y'know."

Yes, I knew. She finally had her tubes tied after many broken

55

appointments. Wasn't it just like Shirley to want a baby and make Vicky go through with the pregnancy.

"Vicky, whatever you decide, we have to have your Mom's co-operation. So why don't you tell her today, and both of you come and see me tomorrow."

Several days passed with no sign of Shirley or Vicky. I finally telephoned.

"Did Vicky talk to you about—"

"You mean about her baby?" My heart sank. I knew the decision.

"Yes, did you discuss it with her?"

"Yes, I decided that she'd have it. I'll look after it and she can go on to school."

She will look after it all right, I thought bitterly, the way she looked after her own kids.

One of the subtle nuances of deciding whether or not to continue a pregnancy is the emotional neediness of the teenager's mother. Often the mother feels that her child is no longer in need of her—she is a grownup, with her own life to lead. This brings on a strange feeling of loneliness, coupled with a sense of growing older, and often, of not having a purpose in life any more. Mothers, particularly those who have centered their lives on their families, often feel that they can somehow stop time passing as long as they have a baby to care for.

When confronted with a pregnant daughter, this need is fulfilled two ways. First, the daughter needs her mother, often for the first time in several years.

Second, the baby itself is a continuation of the mother's usefulness in her role as parent. Someone needs her, and this makes her feel fulfilled.

The mother of many a teenager may firmly believe that she is being self-sacrificing in suggesting that she take care of her daughter's child. But more often than we know, her decision comes, not from what may be best for her daughter, but from her *own* emotional needs.

8
WHAT'S NEW?

Marla came bouncing into my office, unannounced. Appointments were for other people.

"Remember me?" Jauntily.

"Of course, I remember you."

"Well, I haven't seen you for a year."

Something about her drew my attention. She had changed, of course. One year in the life of a teenager is a lot. How old was she now? Seventeen? Eighteen? It wasn't her age—she was grown up at thirteen. Or even her size—she was a big girl with short, thick hair, always neatly combed.

It was her face. There was a glow about it I hadn't seen before.

"Got something to tell you," she said casually as she plunked herself in the chair nearest mine; feet stretched out, a cigarette dangling from her lips.

"Go ahead."

"This is going to be a shocker, even coming from me."

"Come on, cut the drama. Tell me or don't. Please yourself."

Knowing her as well as I did I knew this would be a challenge she could not resist.

She looked at me speculatively.

"OK." She sat back in the chair, lighting another cigarette, knowing well that smoke irritates my eyes. She looked at the smoke from her cigarette curling up to the ceiling and out the window.

"I'm pregnant," she said casually, turning to face me, enjoying the effect, yet tensely watching, awaiting my reaction.

"You are *what?!*"

"I told you this was going to be a shocker."

"I mean," I spluttered a little, obviously flustered. "You can't be!"

"Why not?"

Why not indeed? Biologically there was no reason for her not to be. But Marla was a lesbian. She had known this since she was nine years old.

Well, many things impossible for most people were everyday matters for Marla. She had packed more living in her seventeen years than most people experienced in a lifetime.

What came next was another shocker.

"And know what? I'm gonna keep the kid."

I stared at her speechless.

"I know what you'll say, but I'm gonna keep her or him, so if you wanna pull for me, I'll stay; if not, I'll manage by myself, as usual."

This was far different from the first time when Marla had marched in, in deep trouble, and managed to get me to help bail her out. But this was different. My mind raced. My voice, my manner had to be just right; otherwise, she would bolt.

Casually, my inflection neutral, I said, "OK, why don't you tell me about it, that is, if you feel like it?"

"Naw," she teased. "Not now. I'll let you simmer for awhile—do you good. Be seeing you."

And she was gone. That brat! She knew how to get to me, how to manipulate me every time. Oh well, she'll come back in no time, I thought smugly. But she didn't.

Her next visit was equally dramatic. She brought in the baby to be immunized and proudly displayed him.

Sean really was an attractive baby. He was wrapped in a hand-knitted, blue and white shawl.

"I bet you thought I couldn't do it, I mean, have a baby and all that. Well, I did it!

"Well, be seein' ya, s'long," And off Marla trotted, looking proud and holding the baby with ease and tenderness.

My next encounter with Marla was not exactly an encounter, just a phone call. A subdued, quiet, tense voice:

"Gotta see you. I can't take it any more."

This was alarming, she sounded too quiet, unlike her somehow.

"Can you come at. . . ." I was prepared to clear the decks for her.

"No, I can't. I can't leave the baby. I'm alone. Can you come, like maybe tonight?"

"I'll be there."

58

Click!

The phone rang again.

"Got my address?" A bit of the jauntiness crept into her voice. "So how do you expect to visit?"

I didn't know what to expect. She always managed to get along financially. She never went on welfare or had any dealings with agencies. How she did it I did not know—and did not want to find out.

When I arrived, I was pleasantly surprised to see her living in a three-room apartment which was tastefully furnished and clean. Before I could catch my breath, she shot the first question at me.

"Can they take my baby from me if I'm a lesbian?"

"What brought that on?"

"Tell me!" Her face was tense, white, anxious. "I have to know."

"Nobody can take a baby from a responsible mother. Gross negligence and maltreatment has to be proven."

"What's gross negligence? Like leaving the baby alone and no feeding, that sort of thing?" She didn't wait for a reply.

"Well, yes, partially."

"Oh, OK." She seemed relieved.

"This woman I was living with—we had a real blowup. She accused me of all sorts of things. I was running around on her—y'know all that stuff. So I just told her to go to hell and I moved out. But now she's threatening to have Sean taken away. Listen, I've been going to school, getting real good marks, pretty soon I'll finish grade twelve and I'm gonna go into some profession. I can make it if my past doesn't catch up with me."

"Good for you. I didn't realize you had all that ambition."

"Well, the kid made a lot of difference in my life. I had him to straighten me out and it's working." She glanced sideways at me trying to read my reaction.

I didn't say a word.

"That's why I'm scared. If they take him from me I know I'll slip back, and well, I want to be a good mother."

Then she suddenly asked, "Do you think I should get married to give Sean a father?"

That was some curve she served me. The one thing I knew about her, but did not know exactly why, was that she hated men with a passion that was greater than any feelings expressed by lesbians or "straight" women I'd encountered.

59

"Well," I was cautious. "That depends on how you feel about men now. Unless you've changed radically, I would think three times."

"OK, OK, it was just a thought. See, I haven't had anyone with me for a long time. Sean's getting to an age that he might notice, ask questions. I want his life to be better than mine was. I'm determined to make something of myself so I can be really self-supporting, but I don't want to screw him up emotionally."

She had changed. I marveled at Marla and was inwardly proud of her.

About four years later she breezed in. She had changed remarkably—more mature, tastefully dressed, considerably slimmed down and carried herself with an air of self-conscious awareness.

Her first words were typical.

"Hi! Remember me?"

"How can I forget?" And we both laughed.

It was good to see her. She seemed in fine form and bursting to talk. "Where have you been all this time?"

"Oh, around," she teased. "Did you worry about me?"

"No. I know that you know how to look after yourself."

"Well, not all the time. Sometimes I need advice from pros like you, so I came. . . ."

"How's Sean? He must be big."

"Yup. He's six, gorgeous, polite, intelligent—just like his mother." Her eyes were alight, twinkling at me, teasing, daring me to banter with her.

"Actually, he's a nice kid. Hey, know what? I got married."

She sat back, enjoying the effect, smiling triumphantly. "Didn't think I could do it, eh?"

"You know what?" I said trying to hide what I really felt. "I've come to the conclusion that you can do anything you set your mind to do."

"Remember I told you I was worried that Sean should have a normal upbringing? Well, I decided he needed a father. This guy, he's loaded but he needed a wife." Her eyes twinkled. "If anybody found out he was gay, his fancy career would go, like kaput. So, he knew me and made an offer—a real generous one."

"But . . ."

"You don't approve. I can see it in your face."

"Well, it's OK when Sean is young, but he'll grow up and—well, he'll catch on."

"Not to worry." She said cheerfully. "I'm divorced. Gotcha!" She sighed. "Yah, you're right, it did not work. We both realized it soon enough, but he adopted Sean so he can inherit, y'know when he kicks off. And Sean, well, he can say he has a father. He's at school now and kids ask questions."

"But what about the future?"

"Well, he sees him—like he is really his father. He's real nice to Sean. And it's easier for me. Approve?" Half taunting, half teasing, daring me to be critical.

"Look, it's your life and you live it as you see fit."

"Yah, I know." She sat for a while, pensive, suddenly both sad and unsure of herself. "All my life—" Then fiercely, "I'm determined to give Sean the best I can get for him. I will not allow him to suffer what I suffered. He didn't ask to be born. It was me who wanted him, so, it's up to me.

"I love Sean more than my life. But will I understand him when he gets older? How will I guide him to be a decent human being? How should he relate to women?"

She terminated the session by saying in essence: "It's been good for me, but I still can't come to terms with all the damage that was done to me. Just once, I'd like to see a so-called normal family that works. But it sure is an awful responsibility to bring up children."

She brightened, and got her old teasing look on her face. "Well, I guess I'll just have to play it by ear. Bye."

9

WHY ME?

She was awakened from a deep sleep by a sharp, searing pain through her abdomen and back. It felt like sharp pointed knives pushing deeper and deeper into her flesh.

Her scream brought her mother into her room.

"What is it, what's the matter?" Her mother's anxious voice and troubled eyes floated nearby.

She could not speak nor move. She gulped for air like a fish out of water, unable to speak, not knowing what to say or do.

Suddenly she felt a gush between her legs. The pain eased up, but did not disappear.

Her mother lifted the covers, "Oh my God!" She swiftly brought some towels and phoned the ambulance.

The next few hours were a blur of pain, running feet, whispering voices, and needles being stuck into her.

When Pat awoke the next day, the sun was streaming in through the partially curtained hospital windows. She felt weak, but comfortable. She lay there with eyes closed, savoring the good feeling. She hadn't felt good for a long time.

About a week after the miscarriage, she came to see me. She looked pale and drawn. At fourteen, she looked like a winsome child, untouched until now by tragedy.

Silently weeping, she sat looking out of the window. When she spoke, it was as if from far away.

"Remember our talk when I first got pregnant, when Mom wanted me to have an abortion? I didn't want one. I wanted a baby. I know it wasn't practical or realistic—all the things my Dad wanted me to be. Everybody pressured me. But I just wanted something of my own.

"Remember how you said those things about how dangerous it was for me. Like, I didn't believe you. I said to myself, 'She's making it up to frighten me, to change my mind.' Now I know, now I know. But why me?"

She turned her tear-stained face to me. "Why me?

"It's funny." Her voice was sad, suddenly more adult, more knowing. "It's the one thing I wanted, something of my own, all mine, just mine. Well, now my parents will be happy. I'll be practical and realistic, finish school. Maybe even do something useful." She got up slowly.

"Sorry to be such a baby." She smiled ruefully. "Thanks for everything."

For whatever reason a teenager gets pregnant and carries to term, whether she wants the child; whether she has been too frightened or uninformed to do anything about it until it was too late; or whether she or her parents object to abortion on principle, the fact remains that teenagers take grave risks by carrying a child. This is especially true for younger or not fully developed bodies.

While doctors, nurses, and other health workers are fully aware of the risks, the public is by and large ignorant of such matters.

Ironically many teens and their parents regard the pill as dangerous, yet remain unaware that pregnancy is by far the greater danger.

The risk of maternal death for pregnant teens under fifteen years of age is sixty percent higher than that for the general population[1]. The dangers for the unborn child are also substantially above the national average.

Some of the more common prenatal problems for teenagers are listed below. This is not an attempt on my part to scare young people, or to put undue pressure on them to have an abortion rather than carry the child to term. The dangers do exist, and I have seen too many examples of young women suffering unnecessarily because they are unaware of the possible complications of pregnancy, or simply because they are too afraid or too uninformed to get proper prenatal care from a doctor.

One of the common complications which faces a teenager during pregnancy is hypertension or high blood pressure and pre-eclampsia. Some teenagers may even have hypertension before they become pregnant and not know it. It usually starts with headaches, blurring of vision, dizziness and can lead to *eclampsia* or *toxemia*.

63

The hands and feet will swell due to retention of fluid in the tissues. If unattended, the teenager will experience pain in the upper abdomen. If medical help is not sought, severe convulsions may follow; these may result in the death of the mother and baby.

It is therefore imperative that if any of these symptoms are noted, the teenager should be taken to a hospital immediately because once convulsions set in, it may be too late for both the mother and the baby.

Another serious complication, which occurs more frequently than is recognized, is what is termed *premature* labor. When less than eight months pregnant, the teenager experiences painful contractions in the uterus. During these contractions, the membranes rupture (the "water breaks"). This makes for a very difficult situation.

Premature rupture of membranes brings serious complications to the baby and mother. When membranes rupture, the potential for infection exists and immediate admission to a hospital is vital to protect mother and baby from possible death.

In many teenagers, particularly those under sixteen years, the pelvis usually is not fully developed; in fact, it is often underdeveloped. In other words, the baby may be too big for the young girl's pelvis. This is referred to as *caphalopelvic disproportion.* This poses a problem, as the baby cannot be delivered through the usual means, via the cervix and vaginal canal. The only way to deliver the baby is for the teenager to have a cesarean section. This, of course, is major surgery, necessitating an incision in the abdomen and then the uterus.

One of the most harrowing experiences is prolonged labor. When labor sets in, the fetus is supposed to move down head first with each contraction, ready for delivery. However, in prolonged labor, the contractions take place but no progress is made: the baby does not move. In this situation, a caesarian section must be performed to remove the baby from the uterus.

In most pregnant women, the blood volume increases to one and a half times normal volume. Naturally, this increases the woman's iron requirements. The mother needs to supplement iron for the baby as well. Teenagers are well known for their poor eating habits. They tend to be nutritionally deprived, anyway, and if they are pregnant, often become anemic. It is therefore of paramount importance that iron supplements and proper nutrition be made available to the teenage mother. Poor eating habits and lack of medical care often increase the likelihood of gestational diabetes. Many teenagers deny their pregnancy, even to themselves, and go on a starvation diet to lose weight. The only result is harm to themselves and the baby.

A further danger for teenagers is an abnormal (very rapid or very slow) heart rate in the fetus. If left unattended, this complication may result in abnormalities or death of the fetus. There are no recognizable signs that the mother can observe: only a doctor can make the proper diagnosis.

Another critical problem in general well-being is the frequent use of tobacco, alcohol, and drugs. Such habits are addictive and introduce further problems for the fetus: drug dependency, alcohol syndrome, etc. Teenage pregnancies often occur in the presence of sexually transmitted diseases and other infections which are very harmful to the fetus. The most common of such venereal diseases are gonorrhea or syphilis.

A Problem of Attitude

The mortality rate for infants born to teens under eighteen is almost double that for infants born to mothers in their twenties. Infant mortality data indicate that six percent of babies born to mothers under fifteen years of age die in their first year. This rate is twenty-four times higher than for babies born to older women.

A Johns Hopkins childhood development study which followed up the children of teenage mothers for twelve years found that these children generally performed less well in school and had repeated a school grade more often than children of older mothers.

It is obvious that many of the risks to both mother and fetus can be greatly reduced through proper prenatal medical care and adequate nutrition.

Teens must be encouraged to report to doctors earlier in their pregnancies. Many teens spend the first three months trying to find ways to tell their families of their condition and do not see a doctor until the fourth month or later. Far too many wait until they are more than six months pregnant. For medical care to be most effective it must begin as soon as possible. The program must be followed conscientiously by the teen mother, who often lacks sufficient motivation to attend regularly.

"The nurse keeps on hassling me."
    "What about?"
    "She wants me to attend those classes about my kid."
    "You mean prenatal classes."

"Yah, I guess so. They're dumb, and I don't want to go."

"Why?"

"It's too much trouble; I'd rather stay at home, you know."

"And watch the soap operas?"

"What's wrong with that? I like the stories."

"Don't you think you could sacrifice one afternoon a week and learn all about how your baby develops, do exercises, and meet the other kids?"

"So how is that gonna make a difference? I'll have the baby with or without classes."

Every health worker or counselor involved with pregnant teenagers has experienced great difficulties getting girls to attend classes regularly. Doctors and health care workers must make every effort to impress upon these girls the real risks to their lives and that of their infants if proper prenatal care is not adhered to.

One of the greatest contributors to poor performance and ill health in infants born to teenage mothers is inadequate prenatal nutrition.

"How are you doing?"

"OK, I guess."

"You look a little pale."

"I'm OK, just getting fatter and fatter."

"Well, the baby has to have room to grow."

"I'd like to put that kid on a diet."

"You're kidding, of course."

"No, I'm not. That girl—you know she talks to you about what to eat?"

"You mean the nutritionist."

"Yah, she drives me up the wall."

"Oh come on, she's a very nice person."

"Yah, yah, she's OK but she keeps harping on how much milk, cheese, and all that junk I'm supposed to eat."

"So what's wrong with that?"

"I hate milk and cheese. Besides my Mom's on welfare and she can't afford to buy all that extra stuff for me."

The problem raised by this fifteen-year-old is a common one. Teenagers generally are junk food eaters. They live on potato chips, sugar, coffee, and soft drinks.

There have been numerous and exhaustive studies, all conclusively finding that pregnant women deprived of the proper nutrients, especially during the last three months of pregnancy, can dangerously affect the unborn.

Fifty percent of all mental retardation can be eliminated by proper nutrition. Poor nutrition is also responsible for other abnormal birth defects such as brain damage, which leads to cerebral palsy and learning disabilities. It is estimated that ninety percent of cerebral palsy can be avoided with proper nutrition before birth.[2]

It is also documented that children who are born underweight due to poor nutrition, account for eighty percent of learning disabilities. This, too, can be rectified pre- and post-natally. And the solutions are simple, and inexpensive: if a pregnant mother were given a minimum of a quart of milk a day and enriched bread, we could effectively eliminate these conditions.

Bigger babies are healthier babies, so every effort must be made to impress upon the teenager the need to follow the assigned diet.

The need for comprehensive support systems for teenage mothers is readily apparent. Governments spend billions of dollars providing care services and institutions for the physically and mentally handicapped and the many children of teen mothers who, through a lack of proper physical and emotional care in their early years, are unable to function effectively in today's society. It would require far less financial support if the problems were prevented through the establishment of effective pre- and post-natal programs for teenage mothers.

We must act now and not allow the problems to perpetuate themselves through ignorance, lack of concern, and the inability of health agencies to provide adequate services because of a lack of government support and intervention.

Compared to the real risks of teenage pregnancy and the often devastating long-term effects of this occurrence, the dangers of using birth control pills are minimal indeed. Teens take note of inconclusive articles written about the side effects of the pill yet plunge headlong and seemingly unconcerned into pregnancy with all its attendant risks.[3]

The pill was developed in 1956 and has been on the market for over twenty years. To date there are no conclusive data to prove that the pill harbors inherent dangers for the majority of users. There is, however, conclusive data illustrating the real risks of teen pregnancy.

In addition, a doctor can assess the overall health and lifestyle of a teenager prior to prescribing the pill. He will then follow up and determine any side effects; if they are such that continued use of the pill is not advised, he can then suggest and encourage the use of an IUD.

In the event of pregnancy all assessment and medical care can only be provided after the fact.

Perhaps if both parents and teenagers were made aware of the greater danger of teenage pregnancy, more teenagers would seek protection against an unplanned pregnancy.

[1] Tyrer, L.B. "Complications of Teenage Pregnancy." *Clinical Obstetrics/ & Gynaecology*, vol. 21, no. 4, 1978.

[2] The Montreal Diet Dispensatory.

[3] *Your Health* by Dr. Boroditsky (Obstetrician and Specialist) and Dr. Veena Bhayana (Staff Doctor, Mt. Carmel Clinic) deals with pregnant teenagers.

SECTION THREE

Child Mothers

"It was going to be wonderful. We'd be together all the time, just us. Now we're just alone together."

In the last section we saw why teenagers have babies, but one question remains: having given birth, why do so many teenagers keep their babies? What goes into that decision? And once having made their decision, what lies in store for these child-mothers? What is the reality of daily life, and how could things be different?

10

SHARON

She missed her family, especially her Mom. Her Dad, well, that was different. Somehow, he was always so distant, so remote. But she had to leave.

Sure, she could have stayed. She recalled her Dad's last try—bribery: "You stay, I'll buy you a car. You go—"

A car. So what. She still had to be in at ten p.m. during the week and midnight on weekends. "I'm sixteen," she murmured furiously, kicking the ugly, overstuffed chair. "I'm no baby."

She could not take the fights, the groundings, and the constant hovering over her as if she was made of glass.

Now she faced the counselor, who looked concerned, sort of like her mother. She heard the question from far off; it seemed suspended in the air. All she had to do was reach out and grab hold.

"What are your plans for the future?"

"Plans? What plans?" The question left its suspended mooring and dropped into her lap.

"You know, how you are going to cope with the baby."

"Yes, well, I haven't made any."

It was funny. It's true she had not made any, yet, in a sense she had. She knew one unalterable fact and that was she was going to *keep* the baby no matter what.

"You are entering your seventh month. You have to start thinking, planning." The motherly voice was gently persistent.

She sighed and thought about first meeting Nickie.

She had quit school, found a job as a waitress and also found a friend—easygoing laughing Maria. She had a big family who spoke a strange language, maybe Italian or Portuguese or maybe Greek—she didn't know much about such things. Maria kept inviting her for Sunday meals and the family sort of adopted her.

From the first day Nickie beguiled her. He was a husky, medium-height nineteen-year-old, who worked in the family business.

She had never allowed any guy to touch her, yet she fell for Nickie's charms like a ripe plum. There was gentleness to his lovemaking that made her ache for him, but, at the same time he made her angry.

He never took her anywhere. Just for a drive, maybe a coffee and then to her tiny room. He insisted on secrecy. "Y'know my family." He would turn his bright smile on and put his strong arms around her. "They're old-fashioned, y'know the type—European." She rather liked them.

She asked no questions. But she did worry about getting pregnant.

He pooh-poohed her fears. "Don't worry kid, I'll look after everything. I know what I'm doing."

When she missed her second period, she panicked. "What if . . ." then she thought, "I'll get married. His family likes me. They tell me I'm like family already. They'll be pleased."

Maria invited her to a family party.

When she arrived, she saw many strangers. But what caught her eye was Nickie sitting next to a shy, dark-haired, dark-eyed girl about her own age.

"Here, let me introduce you." Maria dragged her up to this ravishing creature. "Tara, this is my best friend Sharon, and this is Tara, Nickie's fiancée." Sharon stood unable to move or speak.

"No, no," she heard herself murmur, "No, it can't be!" Nickie smiled at her, his arm possessively around his future bride as she silently worshipped him.

How she got home, she couldn't remember.

When she found out she was pregnant, she changed jobs, moved and practically lived in her tiny room.

Time was suspended. She just seemed to wait for things to happen to her.

"Plans? Plans—for what? Oh, the baby—no plans. She and I, we will be together. Just the two of us. We will love each other, and we won't need anyone or anything else. That's my plan." She looked up with a vague tenuous smile, looked up but didn't see anything or anyone, just the dark loneliness surrounding her.

Many girls see their babies as the answer to all their problems: loneliness, someone to care for or be loved by. The total dependence of a small baby is irresistible. Full of ideas about building a tiny nest of security, away from the pain of the world, these teenagers fail to see the trap they are setting for themselves.

For their security is really a terrible isolation. Cut off from the outside world, they feel increasingly resentful of their imprisonment. They grow angry and frustrated with the tiny person who demands continual attention and cannot understand nor fulfill any of the mother's longings or needs.

As we will see later in this section, it is this type of situation that so often leads to neglect or abuse, when the mother, who is unprepared for the life she has committed herself to, cannot cope any more, and lashes out at the only person she can—her child.

11

PLAYING HOUSE

As she sat in the drab, cheerless room, Julie's thoughts wandered. She is five years old again, watching her mother packing or rather throwing things together. A taxi—the door bangs and she is gone. She is growing up. She has a small, pinched face and pleading, brilliantly blue eyes. Her small, thin body stands quietly, hugging a wall.

She shivered, as she remembered the many beatings from her father; the ugly, angry face of her teacher, because Julie did not understand; the giggling and hostile glances of her schoolmates at her ill-fitting clothes.

And Jim. She was so happy with Jim. Even when he was drunk and angry, he was better than her father and a houseful of brothers and sisters who were always squabbling and fighting. She hated them with a passion.

The lady at the agency had been so kind. She had explained all about Julie getting a nice apartment, well, not yet, but when the baby came. All about mother's allowance, and how there were a lot of girls like her, and she would have friends. She explained how having a baby wasn't frightening like people say; you just had to love it enough, and everything else would be taken care of.

Tears welled up in her eyes—what went wrong? She was so happy, she was going to have a baby—a beautiful baby girl. To dress, to play with, to love, yes, to love! She would cook, sew, and everything for her baby. And Jim, of course.

Now he was gone. He, too, fooled her.

She looked around the room. The few pieces of furniture, the tiny stove, even the toaster—all lay broken, scattered throughout the room. He was wild when he got drunk.

74

When the baby came, she was happy. At first she thought the baby would stop breathing, so she stayed awake all night. She would drop off, then awaken with a start and run to the box she had fixed up for her baby.

She was proud of how she looked after her. She washed clothes every day and bathed the baby the way the nurse taught her.

But the baby got sick so often. She knew the room they lived in was cold. She did everything right, but something was wrong.

She was too ashamed to take her again to the Clinic. Maybe they will say she was a bad mother? The baby kept crying. Maybe she was hungry? But she had just fed her.

Wearily, early in the morning, she wrapped the baby up to take her to the Clinic, being careful to put clean clothes on her. As usual, she sat in a corner, quietly rocking the whimpering baby.

Months passed. She now lived in a tiny room with a hot plate and a fridge. The welfare cheques were not enough to cover the rent, the baby's food, and her own. She was very lonely, yet afraid to go out and leave the baby.

Sometimes, Bev across the hall would come over, or she visited her. She was Julie's age, and had a baby, too. But she was bad, Julie decided. She drank and left the baby and went away.

Julie looked after Bev's baby. He was trying to crawl and was into everything. Often she would hear Peter cry. She would go across the hall and there he was, alone. Bev had gone to a bar, she guessed. She would take the crying Peter in her arms and hold him. When he was fed he would fall asleep at once.

Julie sat staring out of the window into the yard next door—a dirty strip of land strewn with broken parts of cars, bicycles, and an old upholstered chair with the stuffing gone, broken springs grotesquely swinging back and forth, back and forth.

Wearily she got up, boiled the kettle, made herself a cup of coffee which she sipped in a desultory fashion.

This was her birthday. Julie was seventeen.

How does a teenager like Julie get into this situation? When a young girl gets pregnant, she is terrified, and her first instinct is to find someone to take care of her—to make everything better again. Often this person is a counselor or social worker, who can be seen as someone who can work miracles.

But the type of miracles she works often depend on her own attitudes on unwanted pregnancy, abortion, and single parenthood. If she is deeply against single parents, and has little faith in the ability of young parents to cope, she may encourage the young girl to have an abortion. And there may be cases in which a girl, convinced against her own better judgment, suffers emotionally because of this decision.

But the graver risks seem to be from the other miracles, the promises that those opposed to abortion under any circumstances offer. For they have more romantic appeal to the young. Promises of sufficient income to cover expenses, help with accommodation and day care, sometimes even promises that the mother will be able to return to school or train for a good job—these are hard to turn down. And when, perhaps through no fault but that of over-simplification by the counselor, it doesn't have a happy ending, the girl is unable to do anything about her situation. Once again, she has been betrayed by the very people who were supposed to be helping her. Once again, she is alone, without the means or the freedom to better her lot. For the kind of determination it takes to get out of this type of situation takes more perspective and maturity than most teenagers have.

12

VELMA

She woke up one morning feeling miserable—tired, washed out, and sort of dizzy. Then the nausea came. She made a wild dash to the bathroom and vomited everything she had in her stomach. She kept retching, but nothing would come. She bent over the toilet bowl—the sweat pouring down her face and armpits, her face beet red—afraid to move.

Finally, Velma washed her face, rinsed her mouth out and returned to the bedroom she shared with her kid sister, Gail. She was fun-loving, lazy, got away without doing her share of the work and tattled even if it wasn't true.

Velma was a quiet, shy fourteen-year-old. Being the oldest she was responsible for the six little ones. She got the kids up to ready themselves for school. Most of the time they were pretty good because the bus picked them all up. They had to be ready early and out there at the farm gate waiting, rain or snow. If you weren't there, tough, the bus driver would honk once and then, with a screech of the brakes, he'd be off.

Her parents were quiet, hard-working, God-fearing people. They did not talk much, just did things together, and anticipated each other. She loved them, their quiet ways, and the stern but kindly way they disciplined the kids. Sometimes Velma wished they did not have to work so hard and look so, well, so sad, as if they were worried.

They did not show much affection, but they never laid a hand on the kids. Dad would just quietly, but firmly, tell the kids to behave, and there was no fooling around after that. What she liked best was Mom always saying to the kids, "Now, you mind Velma when we're not around. She's

77

in charge." That gave her authority, but she was too shy and timid to use it. She just helped them quietly, urging this one to hurry and that one to put on a clean pair of jeans. And so it went.

That's only why she felt so awful this morning. She hated to be sick. It meant the kids might be late and miss school.

She hurried to wake the kids up.

Timmy waited for the bus with them. The kids ran to him noisily greeting him. She had known him since they were kids and played together. His family's farm was just a few hundred feet away, sort of kitty-corner. All his brothers and sisters were married and had moved away. In a way, he was an only child. They greeted each other with apparent casualness, but she felt a warm flush whenever she saw him.

This morning, she felt different. She didn't know why. Maybe because she felt so miserable. She felt weak, queasy, and sort of disinterested. He sat next to her as usual, and reached for her hand, which he usually held hidden under the books on her knees. But she turned away staring out of the window.

He looked puzzled and tried to touch her long, heavy braid. She pulled it over her other shoulder, out of reach.

He was a tall, well-built boy of sixteen, smart at school without trying. He was fun, always doing goofy things, usually to make her laugh. But he was stubborn too. When he wanted something, he kept at it. Outside of that, she liked him. He often helped with the kids and was always hanging around the house. Mom and Dad liked him.

As the weeks passed, Velma continued to be nauseated but not as bad as the first time. She wasn't sick or anything; she just could not stand food, so she ate next to nothing. That helped a bit.

When she did not get her period the second month, she started to worry. As the weeks passed, panic set in. She was frozen with fear!

She could not believe that it could happen so quickly. They just did it twice. So how could it be?

She remembered feeling shame and guilt all over again. The first time was at her house. She was baby-sitting. Mom and Dad went to a wedding and told her they would be very late.

"Would she like Timmy to keep her company?" They were so trusting. She blushed just at the thought that she had done something that would hurt Mom and Dad so badly. Especially her Dad; he was so proud of her, always nodding approvingly when she brought her report card with A's and B's. Her Mom, well, her Mom might be more understanding.

Timmy had arrived as usual, loaded with chocolate bars and sunflower seeds; they both loved to watch TV and eat.

They watched a late, late movie which was a love story.

Timmy kissed her as usual, but something came over him. His hands were everywhere, all over her body. She liked most of it, except when he took off her panties and pushed into her. That hurt! But he apologized, looking scared. She straightened her clothes up and pretended nothing had happened.

The second time was on the shore of a small lake. They had bicycled and were hot and dusty when they got there. He went behind a bush, dropped his clothes and just dived in. She sat there hot and dusty, with everything sticking to her. He kept urging her to jump in, and he promised not to look. Finally she did.

He got out first, offering a towel on the grass—the only one he had— and promised not to peek. When she was almost dry, he stole behind her, held her against him, and once again his hands explored her body. Enjoying it all, she stood quietly, feeling good all over. Her mind empty, she just wanted it to go on forever.

This time she enjoyed it more. Then guilt, mingled with shame, gripped her. She pushed Timmy away, and vowed never to let him do it again ever!

And that was all. Now, all she felt was terror.

She continued to drag herself around, afraid it was written all over her face. Timmy tried to make her tell him what was wrong. But she held back the tears, and just turned silently from him.

Her mother watched her worriedly.

One day, toward the end of the school year, she felt too sick to go to school so she stayed home.

Her mother came up and sat by her bed. In her usual, quiet, sad voice she said, "You aren't pregnant, are you?" Velma turned away, sensing the hot flush that suffused her face. As she shook her head vigorously from side to side to convey no, tears came rushing down her cheeks belying her no.

With a deep sigh her mother left the room. She came back to tell Velma that she had made an appointment to see a doctor. Terrified, Velma nodded acquiescence.

When they arrived in my office, I was struck by the quiet desperation of the parents, and the wide, frightened eyes of their daughter.

The father was a tall, thin man with high cheekbones, longish face, and eyes sunken with a strained look. Fine lines around the eyes bespoke of worry rather than laughter. He kept his work-worn hands on his knees, grasping his knees now and again to reveal agitation.

The mother was small and bony rather than slender. She sat straight, her back not even touching the back of the chair. Her hands—chapped, nails broken—rested on her purse which she kept grasping tightly with knuckles protruding.

She began, "The doctor in our town sent us to you. We don't know what to do. She is so young."

Father looked grimly ahead, hardly opening his lips; the words came with difficulty. "We never expected nothin' like that to happen, we trusted her. We thought maybe you can tell us—she's so young, maybe she should get married."

"Is that what she wants?" I asked quickly.

"We didn't ask her."

Velma's eyes took on a glazed look, her face went blank; she sat perfectly still, utterly rigid.

Father spoke again. "We are not educated people. We work hard all the time. The wife and I want to give our children a better life. Now I don't know what to do." This was a long speech for a man who seldom spoke.

His wife seemed to gather courage, and spoke in a hardly audible voice while looking fixedly at her shabby purse. "I, that is, we maybe are to blame. Velma, well, she was left to mother the other children. There is lots to do on a farm, just the two of us, and what with children coming often, well, we kinda expected too much from Velma, leaving her with them kids to mind." Face aflame, a deep sigh, eyes on the purse.

"Perhaps we should discuss Velma's pregnancy and what is the best thing to do for all concerned, especially Velma's welfare and the baby's," I ventured.

"We ain't gonna kill it, and that is a fact!" The father's tone had a finality that did not encourage discussion.

"All of you go home and think things over very carefully. It's early in her pregnancy. All sorts of decisions are possible. You should consider Velma's schooling, her future, talk to her, find out how she feels. . . ."

He interrupted me, quietly but firmly. "She's our responsibility, we will go now and let you know."

His getting up was a signal. His wife, her face a mask of sadness and bewilderment, made a cautious step toward him but stopped as if by command. Velma just sat, expressionless, pale eyes staring into space. She tried to get up, but when her father spoke about marriage, something in her froze. She wanted to explain, but she couldn't speak.

Gently I touched her shoulders, quietly urging her to go with her parents. I raised my voice so that her parents heard. "She can come to see me, can't she? You will let her come to see me? Maybe she wants to discuss this by herself. Is it OK with you?"

"She can come if she has a mind to."

She followed them like a sleepwalker.

During the weeks that followed, we held several more discussions. The parents had many fears and concerns. But no abortion, no adoption. On these two matters, they were firm. The rest, well, they didn't say much; they just talked around the subject, without real plans or firm decisions. Velma remained silent.

Velma continued with her schooling. She ate very little—at first, she was constantly nauseated; later, she just didn't feel like it.

When school was over, she quit coming to the doctor. When she thought she was beginning to show, she stayed in her room. She would go for a walk when it got dark.

Her parents and Timmy's talked a lot, but they didn't discuss anything with her.

Timmy would try and see her. She avoided him. One evening while out for a walk, he suddenly appeared, thrust an envelope at her, and ran off.

When she got home, she locked herself in the bathroom and opened the letter. A single sheet with his familiar scrawl jumped at her.

Dear Velma:

Maybe I'm scared, or something, but Mom and Dad and your parents want us to get married.

I'm sorry, I can't do it. I didn't mean to hurt you, honest to God, I didn't. You see, I really love you, honest. I wish I could be with you, but it is no good. I guess we're both too young and so I'm taking off.

Love,
Tim

She wished she could disappear and never be seen again. She could not stand being with the family. The noisy bickering among the kids, her sister's shrill voice trying to drown them out. So, one day, she climbed up to the attic, put her aching back on the floor, and just lay there, inert, staring into space.

The next day her father brought in a cot they had in the cellar; he and Mom dragged up an old bureau that had belonged to Grandma. Her mother brought bedding and moved her clothes in.

Her father was up in the attic every minute he could spare, fixing it up to make a real room out of it. She was so grateful but ashamed and guilty. The guilt ate her. It was her fault, her Mom and Dad had plenty to do without adding an extra burden. She wanted to fall on her knees and ask their forgiveness, but she couldn't. She remained motionless and silent. She could sit for hours staring into space. Sometimes she would think, "It's all a mistake. I'm not pregnant. How could I be." She tried to block out the memory of Timmy and the lake.

Her hatred of herself was awesome. The thought of looking big terrified her. It was her mother who was always big, pregnant with one of her sisters or brothers. She had felt ashamed to see her mother so gross. It was obscene—her mother waddling like a duck with her huge stomach. Always working to the very end.

One day her father brought in an old sewing machine. Just put it down and left. She sat staring at it, not moving.

Ever since she was eight she had helped her mother with the sewing. She was really good at making skirts, blouses, and shorts. She made her own clothes.

Then some material appeared.

"I must be getting big," she thought, wishing for the hundredth time she could die.

When she could no longer button up her jeans, she cut the top on both sides and sewed in an elastic to keep them up. Several weeks later she finally made a skirt that wrapped around her body, and a big blouse.

Still silent, eating very little, she tried to help her Mom—cooking the meals, mending the kids' clothes.

When the pains started, she refused to acknowledge the signs. The doctor's nurse had told her again and again what would happen, but she still fought the reality.

Her mother must have heard her whimper. She put her in the car and drove to the hospital. Velma's daughter was born the next day. The whole thing was a blur of pain.

She lay there miserable, wishing she were dead. She felt her stomach— it was soft and much flatter. "It's over," she sighed and fell asleep.

When they brought her daughter, she looked at her the same way she did when her mother brought a baby home. It wasn't hers, but somebody else's. The blotched little thing appalled her.

Her mother took them home late one afternoon. Velma wearily climbed the stairs to the attic and threw herself on her bed. A crib awaited the baby.

She looked after the baby's physical needs with the automatic proficiency of caring for her brothers or sisters. But she never played with the baby nor talked to her.

She was numb, unable to think, plan, or speak. She hid when someone came to visit.

The months, years passed. When the baby began to walk, she moved her downstairs with her sisters and brothers. Her daughter called her grandmother "Mommy," copying the other kids. No one corrected her, least of all Velma.

She worked harder than ever, helping her parents whenever they needed her. She only spoke when it was necessary; she was very patient with the family, never complaining, never asking for anything.

Her main interest was sewing. On her eighteenth birthday her father bought her an electric machine. She sewed for the whole family, except for herself. She just wore anything her sister did not want.

At eighteen, she looked thirty.

The years passed, and Velma remained on the farm, silent and alone.

Velma's Parents

Velma's parents were gentle, kind, and loved their daughter. They were God-fearing, hard-working people, eking out a hard living from their small, isolated farm.

They did what their parents would have done. Try to marry Velma to Timmy, so as not to bring shame on her. When Timmy took off, they did the only other thing within their experience—solve the problem within the family.

They were not verbal people. It did not mean that they did not hurt for their teenage daughter, but they kept silent as was their custom.

Living in a rural setting, far removed from neighbors, families like Velma's become insular. The routine, the daily drudgery, drains them and leaves them little time or energy for anything more than survival. Their pride and certain desire for privacy intensifies their isolation.

In a small community, a teenage pregnancy gives rise to all sorts of gossip, and parents are reluctant to take their daughter to a rural public health unit.

Most of these health units have prenatal classes which are helpful to explain what is happening, and give advice about how to take care of the mother, what to eat, and how to care for the new infant.

The doctor, too, can play an important role in helping during pregnancy, the delivery and, of course, making available birth control aids to avoid a second pregnancy.

Usually, girls who do not receive all this prenatal care, have a second child within a year or two.

But, admittedly, being on a small, isolated farm makes it difficult to get away for medical care so that often, it is not until teenagers are in their seventh month that parents notice a "change."

Precious time was lost the first six months of not receiving any care at all. Still, with a little effort, care can be obtained, even the low income group.

In Canada medicare is universal. In the U.S.A. only the very poor have medicare which makes it difficult for those above the poverty line to receive care, unless they have private insurance.

13
TEEN FATHERS

I had just finished a talk on teenage sexuality that I had been invited to give to a young men's club group.

The audience was mainly university students although some were in their last year of high school. Most were males, but some had brought women guests. The questions came from the boys mainly.

At the end of the lecture, three of the boys stayed behind and waited for me.

"Would you like to have coffee with us? We want some questions answered." I knew by the tone of his voice that he was troubled about something.

We settled in, sipping our coffee. Carl, tall and lanky, with ruddy cheeks and curly, dark hair, began. "You don't think much of us guys, do you?"

"Come on Carl, she's only giving the girls' point of view." This came from a chunky, twenty-year-old named Allan.

"That's what I mean. From the girls' point of view, the guys are the villains." Carl was not to be deterred.

The third young man was silent. He had straight blond hair, a sensitive face, and eyes that tried to hide pain.

"OK," I said, alert, ready to do battle. "You have a point, I do talk about the girls, because by and large, with the odd exception, they are the ones who are left holding the bag."

"What about some guys? Haven't you come across fellows who are ready to stand by the girl, who want to help?"

"Sure, Carl, there are some who will, and it certainly makes it easier for the girl to go through a pregnancy." I wondered what would come next.

"I don't mean that." Carl was impatient.

"I think we are off track," came a quiet voice. "Why be so pugnacious, Carl, the majority of guys do take a powder and the girl is left alone, carrying the burden that should be shared by both of them."

Allan and Carl looked at him protectively but silently.

"Boys bow out for a variety of reasons. I am in no position to speak for all of them, but some no doubt are irresponsible, miserable louts." He looked embarrassed. "But what do you do when you love the girl, but can't marry her, or even be with her?" He continued passionately. "Some parents treat you as if you are the plague. They don't allow you to enter their house, or even to talk to the girl over the phone—a complete blackout. Suddenly you are poison. All the guy wants to do is help, be with his girlfriend. After all it's his baby, too."

His voice was hardly audible. His friends kept darting anxious glances at him.

"Everybody is for the girl, and that's how it should be. She is the one to assume the awesome responsibility of being a single parent. But there's a limit. The guy is pretty cut up too," he kept on, turning to me. "Do you know what it is like to be suddenly cut off from someone you have cared deeply about? To be treated like a first class heel, when you long to be with her? You want to help but can't do anything except feel helpless because you are just shut out.

"Besides, what can a guy do? He knows he is not ready to marry or even settle down. He knows he has to finish school and go on with his profession. How do you know what to do, what's the right thing?"

We all sat quietly, afraid to move. "OK, OK, it's me, my problem, at least I was in that kind of a bind."

Allan broke the silence. "Look, Dave, you don't have to talk about it. I mean we didn't expect you to. We decided, remember, we were going to have a general discussion about the dilemma guys are in."

"All right, have it your way, but you guys know how I tried to get to see Karen when I found out she was pregnant. It hurts so much to be just shut out as if I didn't exist. Other guys may have similar problems. Nobody knows how hard I tried, at least to be with her, to see my son maybe. My son."

He lapsed into silence, then said quietly, "What's the use? Go ahead. Discuss guys' point of view with her. I think I'll go for a walk."

These boys made a good point. We tend to forget that there are young men who, after making their girlfriends pregnant, are very concerned. Some, it is true, are not allowed to see the girl by her family, and feel hurt and upset that they cannot even be part of the decision-making process. When he is given a say, the boyfriend, as a rule, is very supportive of her throughout the abortion process.

If the decision is to go through with the pregnancy, the boyfriend has to face several realities.

If the girl decides to give up the baby, most adopting agencies give counseling to both parents. But most teen mothers keep their babies. The problem the boy then faces is, does he want to tie himself down? Is he prepared to marry the girl? What about his family? If he is still at school, they may have to help support him and his new family. Would his mother, say, be willing to quit work to look after her son's child? Can he afford to quit school and assume the emotional and economic responsibility for a family himself?

The younger the father is, the more prone he is to pressure the girl to keep the baby, promising, of course, to stay with her. Unfortunately, it usually does not work out.

Boys also face many dilemmas but they have many choices. Some do suffer because, for one reason or another, they are forced to separate from their loved one. The majority, unfortunately, simply walk away from the problem.

Those who marry, even willingly, find that the going is tough.

Facts and figures abound which demonstrate that teenagers who marry because the girl is pregnant are doomed to failure. Such marriages average two years before divorce proceedings begin.

And no wonder! For one thing, financial difficulty is almost inevitable. Kids who have never had any greater financial decision than how to spend their weekly allowance are suddenly supposed to understand budgeting. Money from part-time jobs that used to go on records and clothes now has to stretch to cover rental payments, heating and hydro bills, food for two adults, and diapers and formula for baby.

Most teenagers are not prepared for these harsh daily realities. The usual preconceptions of marriage do not stand up either. Most teenagers see marriage as an escape from the burdensome discipline of family living. No curfews, no grounding, no nagging.

Comes the dawn. With freedom comes responsibility, consideration, the need for perspective and compromise. Neither marriage partner is prepared for this. A big tug of war ensues, often involving the parents of one or both partners.

So it is no wonder teenagers who rush into marriage because of a pregnancy, rush right out. They suddenly find that they are less free now than when they lived with their parents.

She has to stay and mind the baby; he wants to be out with the boys. So they part. And who gets left with an unhappy mother and no father—or vice versa—the child who never asked to be born in the first place.

And who are the victims? The babies. They are the ones who suffer from the inevitable breakup.

Mom and Dad can pick up the pieces after the pain and anguish of the divorce is over and begin life anew. Most remarry and have families. Life goes on.

But children cannot "marry" a father or mother to replace their natural parents. They continue to be torn between their parents who are often so busy with their new lives that they do not notice the hurt and pain that their children suffer. Some only notice if there is a crisis—misbehavior at school, being picked up for breaking and entering, or becoming pregnant. Even then, the onus and the punishment for unacceptable behavior is on the child.

Is it better, then, to remain in a marriage that has become a battlefield? No, that is equally bad.

There should be marriage clinics starting at high school level, but open to all who want to learn the art of coexistence—living together in harmony and friendship. For young people have a lot of growing up to do before they can handle something as problem-ridden as the institution of marriage.

14

TAMMY

The first time, she came to the Clinic with her mother. She was a tall, statuesque blonde, soft-spoken with a ready smile.

They came to confirm that she was pregnant.

Her mother was tall and aristocratic. "Well, we—that is my husband and I—want to do what is best for Tammy, and, of course, what she wants to do." She turned to Tammy with a tender smile.

Tammy blushed, tossed her long golden curls and shrugged, "I don't know."

"My problem is that it would interfere with her studies, her music especially. She has talent, she plays the piano, flute, and guitar."

Why were these well-bred, obviously well-to-do people not seeing their family doctor?

As if she read my thoughts, she continued. "We went to my own physician. I was taken aback by his attitude. He made Tammy feel that she committed a heinous crime. He turned on me, too. Obviously I wasn't a good mother or this wouldn't have happened. I was shocked. How dare he lecture us. I'm afraid we'll have to change doctors. We have heard of your Clinic and, at any rate, here we are."

"How can I help you?"

"Well, abortion is out. Neither Tammy nor I believe in it. I really consider it murder. I'm not against other people doing what their conscience allows them, but I would feel dreadfully guilty if, well, if I were party to it.

"Tammy wants to come here for prenatal care. People are friendly, and, well, I guess you people have more experience, so I'll go along with it."

We discussed the various alternatives. Should Tammy go to a home for unwed mothers? Should she leave the city to visit with her aunt? Should she remain at home?

Tammy sat quietly, looking at us. Finally, she burst out, "I'm not going anywhere. I want to be home, mother, please."

The outburst startled Mrs. Collins. She was so intent on making the proper arrangements that she forgot Tammy should be part of the decision-making process.

"Please, mother, don't treat me as if I was a thing. I have feelings, you know, and I can even think."

"I'm very sorry dear, I just wanted to do what is best for you."

Tammy still in a stormy rage, asked sarcastically, "How do you know how I feel or think?"

"Naturally, we will not send you away if it will make you unhappy."

"I know what's bothering Mom—she doesn't want anyone to know I'm pregnant—that's what. What will the neighbors say?" With that she flung herself out of the room with tears streaming down her cheeks.

Mrs. Collins looked flustered; her former composure was crumbling. She sighed deeply. "She certainly hit a raw nerve. Naturally I'm terrified at the idea of my friends, neighbors, and relatives knowing. My head tells me it's irrational. If she were to give it up for adoption, then I would take her away or send her to my sister and when it's all over, she would resume her life with us. But, it would appear that Tammy thinks differently. I've let her down, poor darling. And she is so young."

She composed herself and soon was her old self again.

"Of course she will stay home. I'll explain it all to the family. I'll call next week, but now I'd better find Tammy."

She found Tammy with a nurse who was trying to comfort her.

Tammy practically lived at the Clinic. She volunteered in the day nursery, playing her guitar and participating in the prenatal classes. She came to believe that having a baby was a natural phenomenon, and she was happy right through her pregnancy. And all the while her mother was very supportive.

During her pregnancy, an old school chum came to town. He would take her out for walks and just be around. She continued her piano lessons, and practiced diligently.

She read every book she could find dealing with child rearing. The various attitudes confused her and she kept asking her mother all sorts of questions.

Her smiling, loving response was always the same. "Just give the baby all the love you have, and make sure he knows it. The Clinic will explain the rest."

When the baby, Brian, was born, they brought him home to a nursery fixed up right next door to Tammy's room.

She was genuinely happy. A mother at seventeen! She couldn't believe it. She loved to cuddle him, to play with him and try to coax a smile from him. Her younger brothers and sisters thought Brian was the greatest.

Her friend kept coming around. He, too, was growing fond of Brian. Gradually, they became lovers—after she had come to the Clinic for birth control counseling and decided to go on the pill. Whenever she came to the Clinic—to have Brian immunized or for herself—she carried Brian in sort of a packsack. Only his chubby legs and head were visible. He was either sleeping contentedly or he was bright-eyed and curious.

One day, she said, "You know, I am lucky. My parents are super. If I want to continue my education, Mom will look after the baby. But I'm scared. You see—" She was uncomfortable and fidgeted. "If I do that, then mother will really become his mother, I'll be the outsider."

She was such a lovely child. "Not necessarily."

"What do you mean?"

"Well, it's not the quantity of caring, it's the quality."

She looked puzzled, not understanding.

"So you will be away all day. But when you come home, set aside every minute of those two or three hours for Brian. Feed him, play with him, put him to bed—the works—then you will not have any trouble."

"But won't he miss me, feel neglected?"

"No, not at all. Children go to nursery school and have fun, then go back to their mothers, and both enjoy each other's company."

While she was making up her mind, she continued to come to the Clinic, and helped out at the day hospital for babies, loving every minute of it.

Finally she decided. She would study piano seriously. That meant being away for four hours. She agonized over that but finally was assured that her family would take over.

When I again heard from her she sent me two tickets for a symphony concert. She was guest soloist. Local girl makes good! And she dropped me a note saying she was married.

She came to the Clinic a few days after the concert.

"Got some news for you." Her eyes crinkled, her smile merry. "I'm pregnant!"

"Are you happy?"

"Oh, yes!"

"What about your career, concert pianist?"

"I've thought about that a lot. Maybe I'm less ambitious than I thought I was. I don't know but I can't be separated from my son any longer. I feel I'm losing him. I mean, he runs to mother for everything. I don't blame anyone; I'm grateful mother was so wonderful, and he obviously adores her. But I want him to know me. I want to be his mother.

"When Ken and I decided to have a baby, we discussed the total situation. Conclusion: I give up touring and settle down. My plan is to open a studio and teach.

"Which brings me to my idea. I want to do something for your waifs. I've been around here long enough to know the problems the poor mites have to contend with. And I want to help. Music is what I'm best at, and, well, I'd like to give free lessons to about five or six kids who show any aptitude in that area.

"I know. You're wondering what they'll practice on. I've thought of that too. I have an old piano. I'll put it in my basement and make sure it's tuned regularly. The kids can arrange their practice hours with me. What do you think?"

"I think it's great."

"So you approve and it's official?"

"Why not. If it doesn't work, I'll demand a refund." We both laughed and hugged each other.

The project was a huge success. The next year she set up an orchestra for all the children. And every week, as soon as I heard the first sounds of "our orchestra," I couldn't resist leaving whatever I was doing to have a look. There were our kids, all from poverty-stricken, unstable homes where love was a commodity, hard to come by, being given the precious gift of music from a loving, generous teacher.

Tammy's Parents

Tammy was lucky. Her parents stood by her, accepting her pregnancy and willing to help on Tammy's terms.

It was not easy for Mr. and Mrs. Collins. Most of their many friends, neighbors, and colleagues would consider a pregnant teenager to be a reflection on the parents.

If their daughters became pregnant, they would either quietly obtain an abortion or ship the girl off to a home somewhere, or take a trip to a distant city to stay with dear Aunt Emily. The baby is born, adopted, and the whole thing hushed up.

It is to Mrs. Collin's credit that she did not force this "easier" route on Tammy. She realized that Tammy's feelings and needs must be taken seriously.

Everything was done to help Tammy during her pregnancy. She received regular care by a doctor; she attended prenatal classes. The nutritionist advised her about her diet, and her family ensured that she ate properly and took care of herself.

The fact that she had a friend who supported her during a period in her life when such a friend was of crucial importance added to her well-being.

Her involvement with music and her later achievements as a musician further helped to make the whole experience less of a burden.

Everything worked out right for Tammy. Given a loving, understanding family, economic independence, an interest in an education and the discipline to accomplish one's goals, a teenager can cope with this stressful situation.

Tammy is a success story. Unfortunately, there are few Tammys.

Most young mothers struggle alone in a shabby one-room, walk-up apartment. The whining demands of the infant saps her strength. The long days stretch into nights; as she longs for affection and warmth, she is somehow supposed to have unlimited amounts to give to the crying baby from whom she can never escape.

The Tammys of this world are the lucky ones.

15

CHILD ABUSE

Her three children nestled closely to her in the big, old, rickety bed which the Clinic had found for her when all her furniture was repossessed.

Ever since Steve had been in jail, she felt numb. Except for her overwhelming fear. She was afraid to go out, afraid to open the door, afraid of the dark. The dark—it threatened to choke her.

Scraps of memory kept coming and going.

When she got pregnant five years ago, she was fifteen. She had known Steve three months. He was tall, fair-haired, and had laughing, blue eyes. She had met him at a party and was flattered that he paid her so much attention.

After all, he was nineteen, much older than the kids she had been hanging out with at school. He was so much fun and generous, too. He took her to fancy restaurants and bought her presents. Her parents did not like Steve at first, but he won them over with his beguiling ways.

When she got pregnant, she told him timidly, terrified he would leave her.

"Hey, that's great. We'll get married. What do you think, kid?" She hated when he called her "kid."

He paid for the entire wedding. He always seemed to have money, although she didn't know what he did. He said he was in real estate.

She had been truly happy. For five years. Her three boys were healthy, happy kids—replicas of Steve, with their straw-colored hair and sky-blue eyes. Amazing! It's as if she was not their mother.

When they arrested him, she couldn't believe it. She was frantic. There

94

was some money in the bank, but it all went for legal fees. The final blow came when every stick of furniture was repossessed. She had been so proud of her home.

She remained in their empty bungalow unable to plan or think of the future. When it was sold, she applied for welfare. How else could she feed her three babies?

Four-year-old Dennis, the oldest, stirred beside her. She held him closely, anxiously peering at his right cheek. It was swollen and turning black and blue. She had been applying cold compresses all night, hoping the swelling would subside and the marks go away.

How had this happened? She couldn't even remember. It was all so fuzzy. He kept whining; he wanted bread and jam, she vaguely remembered. She was out of both. In fact she had little food of any kind. But he kept on and on. He reminded her of Steve when he wanted something and it wasn't there. Raving and ranting that she could do nothing right.

Her fist came crashing into his face—like a piston—suddenly, with a force she didn't know she had. He keeled over and did not move.

My God, what had she done? She held him close, rocking him. Her relief, when he started to cry, was overwhelming.

She must do something. She must hide this from the social worker who was coming the next morning. She ran and got a cloth, put it under the cold tap and applied it to his cheek. He looked awful. When he finally fell asleep, she continued the compresses.

Her violence appalled her. She looked at the other two and shuddered. "God, give me strength not to hurt them. It's not their fault. I must pull myself together."

That icy fear gripped her and would not let up.

What to do, what to do?

She held them close to keep them warm. They, in turn, gave her a comforting warmth. What if it happened again? What if she couldn't control it?

"God give me strength to be a good mother to my boys." But the cold, clammy fear still gripped her.

Abuse of children is widespread. While teenage mothers constitute less than seventeen percent of parents, fifty percent of children are abused by single teenage parents. This means that it is five times more likely that these mothers will abuse their children than older mothers.

They act violently against their helpless offspring out of desperation, hopelessness, loneliness, and fear. Things just get too much for them. Sometimes they think alcohol or drugs will help.

The children, sensing mother's moods, will make more demands in an effort to gain her attention. They, too, are unhappy, bewildered and fearful, knowing that violence is never far away.

Yet these children continue to love their abusing parents. They cling to them and resist being taken from them and placed in foster homes. They, too, cannot help themselves. Yet the more love they demand, the more likely they are to bear the brunt of parental frustration and anger.

16

CAROL

The voice on the other end of the phone plunged right in.

"This is the public health nurse. Have Carol and her kids turned up? I made appointments for them."

"I don't think so."

"Oh, you'd know if she did. Her kids are a mess and so is she."

"What do you mean, 'a mess'?"

"Come on, you know exactly what I mean! Her phantom boyfriend was here. They partied for days, the neighbors told me. He beat her up, as usual, and left to go back up north and—"

"What about the kids, you said they were a mess. How did you get in to see them?"

"My lucky day, that's how. I was in the block visiting another family and I heard the kids crying in Carol's apartment. So the caretaker let me in."

"How—I mean, Carol usually stays with them ... she never leaves them, at least I don't think—"

"Oh, boy, you are pulling for her, aren't you?"

Silence.

"Anyway," she continued, "they were alone, running around in their top underwear—no pants, no diapers. Feces and urine all over the floor."

"So, what about the kids—"

"Well, Joey has a fever and a cough. Linda has *otitis media*—pus running out of her left ear, caking on the side of her face. The other two are covered with impetigo. They've been bitten by bugs a million times. I've had that place fumigated, but nothing seems to work."

97

"What about Carol?"

"Oh, well, she came in while I was there. She said nothing as usual, but I could see she was mad."

"Well, she's afraid the children will be taken from her."

"Darn right they will if I have anything to say about it."

"Well, she knows that," I ventured quietly.

"She doesn't do anything about it, does she?"

I did not want to go into another weekly wrangle with the Children's Aid and the police which we have had many, many times before.

"If that's the state the kids are in, I'll send the car out and pick them up."

"How do you think you'll get in?"

"I don't know. I'll think of something."

Carol was fourteen when she gave birth to her first child. He is now five years old; the other three came a year apart.

She never complained, answered direct questions reluctantly, and sat silently waiting for the doctor. There was something about her that made you want to protect her, to reassure her.

She gave birth easily. Only her eyes revealed the wounds, the terror she must have felt. But not a word, not a whimper.

She lived in a cold, dark basement flat when we went to pick up the kids that day. The old bed never had any sheets on it, just a torn, thin blanket piled in a heap with a bare mattress showing in the four corners. There was just enough room for a bureau with peeling paint so old that the color was not recognizable. The three drawers had no handles, and were open with all sorts of children's clothes hanging out.

The living room furniture was several orange crates holding clothes, shoes, boots, pots and pans. There was a brown chesterfield that sagged to the floor. The stuffing had been pulled out of gaping holes.

The kitchen had two rickety chairs and a three-legged table.

We knocked on the door—scurrying feet, a child's cry, a low voice, then silence.

"Carol, it's the nurse from the Clinic. We want to have the doctor look at the kids."

Silence. We waited. The door opened a crack, then wider. All four kids hurled themselves at us, wanted to be picked up, to be hugged and fondled—neglected, love-starved children, indiscriminately begging for a little love, a little attention.

"Come on, kids, get dressed, we're going to the Clinic to have fun."

They knew what it meant. Running feet, clothes dragged from the bed, under the table, which all but toppled, and out of boxes, and off the floor where their clothes were lying in heaps.

Carol stood helpless, looking dazed. Her eyes were puffy; there were green and brown streaks on her arms, neck, and face—the remains of her weekend beating.

"Carol," I said gently, "Why don't you help us dress the kids and come along with us. There's hot coffee and—"

She gazed at me, a slight fear lurking. Was I taking the kids away from her like the others had done so often?

"Come, Carol, I promise, the kids will be back tonight."

Listlessly she watched the children excitedly follow the nurse to the car.

"Carol, you, too, need help. Come with me and see the doctor. You can stay with the kids and see for yourself. You know the Clinic does not keep children overnight."

As if in slow motion, she searched for her coat which she finally found where she had thrown it in a corner on the floor.

Bathed, hair shampood, sores looked after, well-fitting clean clothes—they were beautiful, happy children. Still clinging and wanting attention, they let go when a hot breakfast was served. But when we brought them toys, they threw them at each other. They did not know how to play.

She sat, sipping her coffee, not touching her food. Silently suffering, watching, not taking her eyes off the children, Carol needed a drink.

Several agencies got together and worked out a plan to help Carol be a better parent: better accommodations, a housekeeper to help her and to teach her to keep house. Yet her drinking was to be tackled somehow. Her new quarters were bigger, airier, cleaner, and warmer. People donated furniture—the children had a room to themselves with two beds. Carol had her own room. She stayed sober and the children were better looked after.

Six months later, Carol and the children disappeared into thin air. A year later, she turned up at the Clinic. Her children were ill, undernourished, with sores all over. Two of the boys had to have their hair cut off to the scalp to get to the infected areas. All of them had bad coughs and fever. They were in the day hospital for months.

Carol was bedraggled. Her face was pale and almost yellow while her eyes stared into space, seeing nothing.

This pattern happened frequently. She would seem to be getting on her feet and then she would just disappear. The Children's Aid tried over and over again to apprehend the children, but Carol always evaded them.

One day we got a call from a neighbor. Strange noises were coming from her apartment. When the nurse arrived, Carol was almost doubled over, clutching her abdomen with both hands, rocking back and forth. The sounds that came from her were a weird cross between a human moan and a hurt animal's whimper.

We practically had to carry her to the car. She did not resist; she just did not respond. It was like dragging a sack of potatoes.

Diagnosis—hysteria.

After an injection she slept several hours. Then came the piercing cry.

"My children. They took my children! I want my children."

The Children's Aid had finally taken them into care. And Carol disappeared again.

Several years later, she appeared in the waiting room. What a change!

She was dressed neatly, with her hair stylishly cut, and wearing just a touch of lipstick giving her a bit of color. Her eyes were bright and alert but still veiled and hidden.

"Carol? Is that you?"

"A-ha."

"How are you?"

"Fine. I came to see you."

Once in my office, some of her anxiety came back. She said nothing for awhile, then, "My kids are doing fine, really good."

"Oh, where are they?"

"With my sister in Ontario."

"I didn't know you had a sister."

"Yah, I have five and three brothers."

I gasped. "Are they here in Winnipeg?"

"Oh, no, they are all over—some at home."

"Where is home?" I was getting bolder.

"In Ontario."

"Do you have parents?"

She nodded in the affirmative. A cloud had settled over her. Then she looked up proudly.

"I'm taking upgrading!" She watched my face.

"Carol, that's wonderful. How are you doing?"

"Fine, I just have my twelve to finish—"

"Carol, grade twelve! How? When?"

She must have read my thoughts.

"Well, I had grade eleven all finished. You know, you have to be tested, and I did good, so they upgraded me and now I'm in twelve."

The whole thing was a miracle. She looked like a teenager.

"Things must be really going well for you."

"Yah, I guess so. I like studying. I was real good at school."

She blushed. Another silence. She began to fidget, stealing glances at me. Suddenly an anguished cry, not loud but full of pain.

"I want my children back."

"You what? I thought your sister—"

"Yah, she's got them."

"But then, isn't she helping you—looking after them—"

"No!" There was so much bitterness. "She wants to keep them all the time—"

"But you're the mother—"

She looked at me gratefully. "I am their mother, ain't I? I am."

"Of course, you are. Surely your sister would—"

"She and her husband are the foster parents."

"Did you agree to this?"

"I don't know, I don't know."

"Carol, what do you want me to do?"

"I want you to try and get them back. You've known me a long time—I have no one else."

"You know I would like to help you in any way I can, but I know so little about you. You never—"

"I know," she said forlornly, "I never talked much. I was—I couldn't."

"Why don't you start from the beginning."

She looked frightened again, staring into space; then, apparently made up her mind.

"If I tell you *everything*, will you help me?"

"Look, Carol, you obviously are in pretty good shape now. You look fine and you are able to study. So listen carefully. I will do all in my power to help, but I must have some facts. What I know about you now will be no great help. Do you understand?"

"Yah, I mean, yes." She sat up straight like a schoolgirl.

And so it came out—the old story: too many kids, an overworked mother, a violent father who beat the kids regularly; finally, her pregnancy and "escape" to Jim.

"Jim was good to me. He never beat me unless he was drunk. Then I started to drink. It made me sick, but it made me forget. Jim worked up north and sent a little money, but it was not enough and, well, I didn't know how to cook or anything, I didn't know how to look after my babies.

"Y'see, I was scared all the time, so scared. I used to lie in the dark hiding under the covers. I tried, honest, I tried. Everybody kept wanting to take my babies. I just didn't know what to do. I watched when you looked after my babies. I tried to do the same, but they cried and cried and I just couldn't keep them quiet. All the time I kept thinking, 'What if my Dad found me, or even my sister.' She always loved it when I was in trouble, and I couldn't let her see me and the babies.

"Sometimes Jimmy would pack us all up and we would go north with him. But he lived in an old shack and it was real cold and the kids got sick. So he'd get mad and drink and hit me. He didn't mean to, he was drunk. Y'see he really lov—liked me.

"When we lived in Winnipeg, I was scared to go out; maybe somebody from back home would recognize me and tell my father."

Of course, this explained her silence, her apparent lack of understanding.

"Once I tried to kill myself."

She was immediately sorry she had blurted it out. "I just wanted to sleep. I thought that somebody nice would take my kids. But I guess I didn't take enought Aspirin. They just made me vomit.

"My sister kept looking for me especially when she got married. She found out through friends of Jimmy's where he was and then, well, she walked into the house and found me. I was real scared, I wouldn't talk to her or anything. But she kept saying how sorry she was and said she'd fix it so that the Children's Aid wouldn't take my kids anymore.

"So we went to live with them. I went off the booze and started upgrading. The kids were real happy. It's a big farm with animals, y'know.

"D'you think, maybe they are better off there?"

That took me off guard. "Well," I weighed each word carefully, "it's a healthy place on a farm. But can't you live there, too?"

"Yah, well, that's what my sister said at first. Now she and her husband fixed it with Children's Aid. They want to adopt them, like for good. I want my kids. I love them. I didn't hurt them, like everyone says. I didn't. I just was so scared—"

She looked at me with so much anguish.

"Look, Carol, this is a legal matter, now. I promise you, we'll get a good lawyer to look into it, OK?"

She nodded listlessly and got up. "Yah, a lawyer. I need a good lawyer, a real good one."

Her words sounded hollow. She knew it was a losing battle.

"I Want My Kids—I Love Them"

A heart-rending cry from a mother, who, in her own way, did love her children and wanted to keep them.

As a child, Carol accepted violence and fear as a way of life.

When, at fourteen she was shown some "kindness" by a young man, she saw him as her salvation. When her father found out about her pregnancy, he beat her mercilessly and kicked her out of the house. Her blind, but natural, reaction was flight.

Whether Jim took her along to protect himself against possible legal implications or whether he was fond of her is a moot point. When Carol found that Jim, when drunk, beat her as her father did, she clung to her children like a drowning person clings to an overturned boat. But she was helpless. Authority frightened her. She was bewildered and numb.

She drank to forget and, in a sense, to survive. She viewed everyone as the enemy. She did not trust kindness; experience taught her not to trust. Her only answer was flight.

What could Carol have done? To whom could she have turned?

The public health nurse and the Children's Aid Society were, in her view, only there to deprive her of her children.

It is tragic indeed, that when she overcame her fear and did trust her sister, she lost her children. It is equally tragic that when at last, she had become sufficiently motivated to upgrade herself and become a functioning adult, it was too late.

17

LORRAINE

Lorraine first came to the Clinic when she was twelve. Her mother, a dark, silent woman, gave all the necessary information, answering brusquely, as if chary of words.

Lorraine sat close to her. When a question was directed at her, she quickly looked at her mother, who answered for her.

When she was asked to undress prior to being examined, her mother gave her a push, hissing, "Do as you're told. Nobody is going to hurt you."

The child stood, shaking.

"Do you want me to tear the clothes off you?" Again the low hiss.

I turned to the mother, "Why don't you leave her to me. Something is frightening her."

"Good luck," she sneered as she walked out.

The child made a move to follow her mother.

I began to talk quietly to her, telling her over and over again what to expect. I promised to stay with her during the examination. I showed her exactly what the doctor would do, while she was dressed.

No response. Finally I said, "You know, we must make sure that the baby in your stomach is not sick."

A wild stab in the dark, but that did it. She began to undress, slowly. I covered her with a gown before she undressed. While she was lying on the table, I explained again what to expect. I told her she could ask anything she wanted, but she just lay there staring, her eyes large with fear.

As the doctor started the examination, she trembled and held on to me, her nails digging into my arm. When I told her she could dress, she just stood there, a lonely little figure, with the large blue gown reaching her toes, the sleeves dangling over her hands.

104

She came alone after that first visit. She usually sat in some far corner with her arms across her growing abdomen and leaning forward so that nobody could notice.

By the time she was in her ninth month, she was well known to the small staff. They brought her clothes, fussed over her and even invited her to their homes. Despite all that attention, she never spoke. We knew, by checking with her school, that she certainly was not retarded; in fact, she was a good student when she attended. But she was always very quiet and had no friends.

She phoned me when her first pains started. I had promised to stay with her during her labor, and because she was only twelve, we were prepared for complications, and had a gynecologist standing by.

I took her to the hospital. Her mother was out. We left a note but need not have bothered. Her mother did not turn up until after the baby was born.

Her labor pains were infrequent but strong. She screamed like a wounded animal, her eyes wild with fear.

Her labor went on for twenty-three hours. She would doze, exhausted, between pains.

Toward the end, she was given a few whiffs of ether. She did not see her baby until she woke up the next day.

It was a beautiful little girl.

A year later, the next and the next, she was pregnant again. I was heartsick. She refused to answer questions about her pregnancies; her mother, morose and angry, refused to discuss the matter, except to arrange to have the three youngest adopted.

Whenever we visited their small house, it was clean. The mother was invariably out.

After the birth of her last baby, we never heard from her again. A new family lived in the small house; they knew nothing of the former tenant.

Ten years later, I received a phone call.

A pleasant, well-spoken voice.

"You probably have forgotten all about me, but I have never forgotten you. My name will mean nothing to you but I must see you. It's urgent! I'll come any time you say—before the Clinic opens or maybe after hours—any time."

Precisely at 4:30 p.m. a tall, slender beautiful woman, dressed in the latest fashion was ushered in.

I searched my memory. Nothing.

She read my mind. "Don't worry about not remembering me. We met fourteen years ago. You haven't seen me for about ten years."

She paused, looking at her hands, not seeing them.

"I have come for a favor, a big favor. If you refuse, I won't blame you. You were good to me when I was a terrified child. You helped, and I paid you back with silence."

It couldn't be. How often had I thought about her, wondering, hoping that she somehow survived the horror of her childhood.

"You remember! You do, don't you?"

I nodded, unable to speak.

"Yes, I'm doing fine. I'm married. You remember my daughter." A shadow crossed her face; she shook imperceptibly.

"I feel if you are to help me I owe you the full story, no matter how difficult it still is to talk about it."

She started again.

"I remember walking through the park, looking at the flowers, rehearsing the things I wanted to tell you. I would daydream that you would take me away from my mother—"

Her voice hardened. "Take me far away, and we would live in a castle and no one would find us. But when I came, I remained silent. My mother's voice, harsh, threatening, lived inside me. 'Don't you dare go and whine to that Mrs. Ross. If you tell her anything, you know what will happen to you.'

"I never knew what would happen to me, but I was too frightened to open my mouth.

"I used to get you confused with my Aunt Debbie. I only remember a little about her, but she lived with us when I was really little. Now that I think about it, my mother must have realized that Debbie would be the perfect baby-sitter. She was loving and kind, and was always there when my mother was not. Apparently, mother gave her room and board, and that was about all.

"I remember the day Debbie told my mother she was leaving to get married. My mother was furious. I thought she would kill her. But I guess it all blew over, and Debbie disappeared. I suspect my mother wouldn't let her see me again, but maybe her new life just took up all her time.

"My mother claims she was deserted by my father. I never bothered to find out if it was true.

"At any rate, lots of men came to visit my mother, mostly at night. I would awaken to loud, drunken voices or strange noises. Once—I must have been three years old— I woke up scared. Maybe I had a bad dream. I went to my mother's room. She was under a man and he was making loud and funny noises. Both were stark naked. She saw me and flailed her arms to tell me to get away. I started to cry.

"The next morning mother beat me with such fury that I was beyond crying.

"Then she took some warm water and carefully cleaned the blood and put some salve on. She kept me in bed for weeks, until I healed. She kept saying over and over again, 'Never tell a soul about your sores, and never, never come to my room at night.'

"Funny, despite the many beatings I got, I loved her. At least I feared being taken from her. Apparently, she, too, was afraid. Whenever the Children's Aid would come, she seemed to know ahead of time, and put on her 'Sunday face.'

"I started to fill out when I was about nine or ten. One day one of her male friends saw me. She ordered me to my room. I heard them argue, then the door banged and he was gone.

"I heard her walk up and down, up and down, like a caged animal. I fell asleep listening to her pacing.

"From that day on, she watched me with a calculated look in her eyes. She spent a good deal of time on the phone.

"One day she sat down after supper when the dishes were done. I was going to my room as usual. She called me back. 'Look, from now on you do whatever my friends ask you to, understand?' I didn't, but I nodded my head 'yes'.

"The next evening she dressed me up in my Sunday best and told me to wait until she called me.

"About nine o'clock she came in to get me. 'Remember, do as you're told. Tell anyone and I'll kill you.' I believed her.

"There was a huge man sitting in the kitchen flushed with drink. He led me into mother's room and told me to undress. I stood staring at him, not moving. He opened the door. 'Tell that kid of yours to take her clothes off, or give me back the money and I'll get out of here.'

"She walked up to me and hissed, 'Get those clothes off or else.'

"Trembling, I took them off and stood silently crying. He didn't even notice. He lay back on the bed, and unzipped his fly. Almost in a trance, he whispered, 'Come here, quick, come here'. I stared unable to move. 'Come here, damn you.' I stumbled up to him. He grabbed my hands, wrapped them around, and whispered hoarsely, 'Squeeze, come on, squeeze.' He helped with his big paws, until there was stuff all over me. He quickly got up, wiped his hands on the bedspread, and walked out.

"After that there were old men, young men, I don't remember. I was forced to do all sorts of foul things. I became numb. When I was eleven and had been menstruating for about a year, I was raped. She staged it; I heard them haggling. He was maybe forty. He wanted me bad; he must have paid lots. I struggled; but he liked that, encouraged it. He stripped me, tearing my clothes to shreds; he pinned me down and got into me, pushing and pushing. The pain was horrible.

"I guess it was inevitable that I would get pregnant sooner or later. Why she let me keep the baby is a mystery to me. Unless she was afraid of the Children's Aid investigation.

"The other pregnancies—well, somehow she managed. I seem to remember a frequent 'client' was either a lawyer or somebody who advised her about things. I got V.D. several times, too, remember?"

How well I remember. She always came when the infection was already deeply imbedded. Her Fallopian tubes were probably ruined.

"We had to leave Winnipeg in a hurry. I don't really know why. Probably the police were on to her. We landed in Toronto. She must have had some money, because she and some guy who was a frequent visitor opened up a small restaurant. We all worked hard, but he kept all the money—just gave us a bit now and then. She was obviously very much in love with him. When he tried to have sex with me, she went into a rage.

"By that time I learned a lot. My daughter and I managed to leave and landed in Montreal quite by accident. I was thumbing a ride and the driver was going to Montreal, so I went with him. He was the first really nice guy I ever met. I told him I was looking for a job as a waitress. He gave me the addresses of some big hotels. Anyway, I got work right away, in a cocktail lounge.

"There I met my husband. He used to come two or three times a week and stare at me. He asked me out and I curtly refused. No man was going to touch me.

"He kept after me for years. I was frightened. He might see my daughter and ask questions.

"I set some goals. Funny, I remembered some of the things you and your students talked about. I was so numb, I hardly heard what you said, but I guess something came through. I worked evenings and studied during the day. Some by correspondence. I finished high school and I'm practically bilingual."

Lorraine

This was said with infinite pride.

"I haven't said anything about my daughter, Adrienne. She is a beauty. She was the only decent thing in my life and kept me going. I loved her with a passion that frightened me.

"I lived with a family who looked after her while I worked and studied. They were good to me, and I was a good tenant—quiet, clean, no boyfriends. After a couple of years George, my present husband, found out where I lived and met Adrienne. He asked no questions.

"George was really something. When he got serious and wanted to marry me I panicked. Finally I decided to tell him that I was raped at twelve and that Adrienne was the result. He believed me and surmised that my odd behavior was related to that experience. I knew nothing about him. He was very quiet but persistent.

"We got married very quietly and lived just outside Montreal near his family, who are very kind.

"Up until a couple of years ago I was happy. I got over my fear of sex. I still don't enjoy it, but I like to please George. But now George wants a child!

"I'd give anything for one. But I can't. Apparently my tubes are shot. I guess my past is catching up with me. He adopted Adrienne, and is a good father, but it's only natural he should want a child of his own.

"Somewhere out there I have three sons."

She wiped away her tears, sat up straight, looked earnestly at me.

"You are our only hope. I'm afraid to ask to adopt a child from the Children's Aid. They might dig up my past. So, I came to you. I need a favor. I need a letter from you saying that you have known me all those years and that I would make a good mother. I need someone responsible to write a letter who has known me for a long time."

She waited, looking at me, pleadingly. My heart went out to her.

"Of course, I'll give you the letter."

She suddenly threw her arms around me, crying with relief, repeating over and over again, "Thank you, thank you. You have saved me again."

Several months later I received a brief note on elegant stationery. Enclosed was a picture of a smiling baby boy.

Meet Doug, the son and heir.
Thanks and God bless.
Lorraine.

Lorraine's Mother

You may have had one of two reactions to Lorraine's story, despite its happy ending. You may have thought, "Mothers don't treat their kids that way, I don't believe it." Or, you may have said, "How much does a woman go through to make her behave that way toward her children?"

If either reaction was yours, here's the story of Lorraine's mother. She may not be typical, but she's common enough that social workers, the police, and community clinics see her all the time. For abused children turn into abusive parents. Lorraine is the lucky exception.

Elsie was in a towering rage when she discovered she was pregnant with Lorraine.

"That's all I need! Damn that stupid Nick, he must be the one. It fits, or is it? Maybe Tony! Tony is too careful, he's not about to be caught that way by his favorite whore," she thought bitterly.

Damn his soul! He was the one who made the "date" for his "friend" so he said. They were all his friends. She felt like clawing his face with her nails.

Yah, Nick paid well. So what? She earned it.

How stupid, stupid, that's all. She usually made her boyfriend wear condoms, but that guy made you believe he really meant what he did when he made love.

He kept coming back every day for a week. She almost weakened, was almost touched. Then he disappeared, just left. No good-bye, nothing. And Tony, playing dumb. She didn't even know his last name. Just Nick—Nick what, who?

Her usual practical side took over. An abortion, that's the answer. It wasn't the first. They were illegal, but doctors did them all the time. But she left the doctor the next day in a blind rage.

"The bastard probably wants more money. Suddenly he has to be careful. Since when? He's under surveillance! Well to hell with him. I'll find a way."

But she didn't until it was too late. The woman told her that her belly was too big and she couldn't do it.

God damn everybody! She'll have the brat and give it up.

But the Children's Aid asks too many questions. Fat chance of anyone taking a baby whose father's last name is a mystery.

But luck played into her hands. One Sunday morning, her kid sister Debbie turned up. She was rather a plain, but pleasant girl of fifteen. Solid, chunky. Her outstanding features were her big green-gray steady eyes. There was a calm about her that even helped Elsie to simmer down. But even Debbie couldn't take it any more at home and had run away.

How well Elsie remembered the back-breaking work in the fields with her mother gathering vegetables, milking cows, washing, cleaning, and looking after the kids. Mother was always pregnant. Ten kids alive, four miscarriages. So, being the oldest, Elsie spent more time at home on the farm than at school. And if she rebelled, the strap with the buckle side was the only answer she got.

She had planned escapes from age eight. Tried a few times and was hauled back. The last time her father chopped off her hair, then shaved her head.

She made good her escape when she was twelve.

She was tall enough and developed to pass for sixteen and worked her way to the city as a baby-sitter or waitress until she could safely buy a bus ticket and come to Winnipeg.

Very early she discovered that men felt there was something about her.

It was Tony who took her in hand. She was about fourteen when he got involved with her and realized her potential. Business partners and sex partners.

When her sister turned up, Elsie had a built-in baby-sitter. Debbie was loving and patient with the growing child, who was quiet, solemn, as a baby.

The whole thing fell apart when Debbie informed Elsie one day that she was getting married and moving to Vancouver.

Lorraine feared her mother, yet wanted her love.

There was much she did not understand about her mother, but she accepted and shook violently whenever her mother gave vent to one of her rages.

Elsie started to see two or three men every night to make money, which she salted away in the bank. An abused child herself, she had no hesitation in using Lorraine to augment her income. Survival was all. No one mattered but Elsie and her precious Tony.

18
THE WAY IT IS

Why, in an age of effective and legal birth control, have teenagers not used protection to prevent an unplanned pregnancy? And why once pregnant, do so many of them go to full term and choose to keep their babies?

The answers to such questions are not simple.

About ninety-seven percent of all girls who do seek birth control have already been sexually active. Despite the availability of a variety of birth control methods, most girls have only a hazy idea as to where to get such information or aids. They have little factual knowledge about how to protect against pregnancy. What they do know, they have picked up from each other or have absorbed as gossip. But most importantly, teenagers become involved in sexual relationships without thinking about possible pregnancy.

Most teenagers are preoccupied with love as a need for affection and attention, and do not think about it in sexual terms at all.

When they become pregnant, they are genuinely astounded. Many go to full term, have their babies, and keep them without any realistic, responsible plan for the future. But why do they choose to keep their babies? Again that elusive quest for love and affection. Most do so because of an innate need to have something of their own to love and to love them in return.

Our stories have also revealed other reasons for keeping a baby. If parents' religious beliefs are such that they preclude interrupting the pregnancy at an early stage, their underaged daughter will have no choice but to carry to full term.

Furthermore, organizations involved in the Right-to-Life movement, such as Pregnancy Distress, advise teenagers to go to full term. These organizations encourage adoption, but many teenagers do not listen. Once they have seen their babies, they choose to keep them.

There are also girls who, in order to hang on to their boyfriends or to force them to marry, deliberately get pregnant. Others are rebelling against parents, whom they seek to hurt. Some, unable to achieve in school and at home, constantly put down by parents, teachers, and others, seek to prove by having a baby that there *is* something they can do effectively.

Society's standards have a profound influence on many girls' decisions to become mothers. The stigma of becoming pregnant out of wedlock, which was so strong even fifteen or twenty years ago, has weakened and, in some quarters, almost disappeared.

Whatever the reason, the fact remains that millions of such youngsters become mothers. And unless something positive is done to help these youngsters and their children, society will reap the whirlwind.

For Teenagers: Coping With Pregnancy

We have seen the hazards a pregnant teenager faces both during and after pregnancy. In order to minimize the dangers, you need proper medical care.

The first step is a visit to a doctor. See a doctor as soon as possible after you suspect you are pregnant. If you do not want to see your family doctor call a community clinic if there is one in your area. If there is no clinic, you can contact one of the nurses at the public health unit in your community or the nearest branch of Planned Parenthood for information on whom to see.

In Canada, there is universal medical coverage. This means the government pays for the visit to the doctor and any tests required. In the United States, you have to pay for the doctor and tests, but public health clinics are less expensive than private ones.

Choose your doctor carefully. Some are very concerned and realize the risks of teen pregnancies. Unfortunately, some do not. A clinic staffed by gynecology and obstetrics specialists is best for you. These specialists usually work in hospitals with high standards, where all necessary facilities are available.

Constant care is a must. A good doctor or nurse will arrange for you to attend prenatal classes. If your doctor fails to mention classes, ask him or contact your local public health unit to find out where the nearest classes are held.

Prenatal classes are important. They provide an opportunity for you to learn about the growth and development of your baby and how best to take care of yourself and your unborn child. You will also learn about labor and how to make delivery easier for both of you. Most prenatal classes include sessions with a nutritionist. She will tell you which food you should and should not eat when you are pregnant to ensure you have a healthy baby.

What About Adoption?

People who put in for adoption want a baby, not a growing child. They also want children whose coloring, hair, skin, and eyes match their own. Babies of mixed races are less easily adopted than single-race babies. They also want a healthy baby.

The increase in teen pregnancy has led to a large number of babies who are victims of drug and alcohol abuse and/or poor prenatal nutrition. Adoptive parents thinking they have a "normal child" may find themselves faced with problems such as learning disabilities and poor physical development.

Hence many babies are left with agencies and are never adopted. Foster placement is also hard to find for such children. Many teenagers, finding the caring for a baby too difficult, give up and leave the child with agencies such as the Children's Aid. Adoptive parents are not too eager to take on a baby who may have had poor nurturing, with possible unfortunate consequences.

Coping With A Baby

Many difficulties confront the teenager who decides to keep her baby.

How these mothers cope depends upon the support systems within their immediate family and community.

Girls who come from a home where parents do help, often do very well. Their mothers take over and care for the baby. The daughter continues

114

with her education and becomes self-supporting. Even if they move out on their own, the extended family is there to keep giving the love and affection so precious for normal development.

Sometimes, however, grandmothers become so attached to the baby that they have difficulty letting go. Many bitter struggles erupt between mothers and grandmothers for possession of the child, sometimes with tragic consequences for all concerned. In such tugs-of-war, the baby can become confused as to who is his real mother.

The problem often arises when grandparents legally adopt the child, during a period in the daughter's life when she wanted out. Then several years later, the mother may marry and settle down, and want her child back.

Healthy, mature support—moral, emotional, and financial—from a loving family can help bring about a happy ending. But, unfortunately, too many parents will agree to help before the reality of a baby in the house along with a frustrated, unsociable, irritable teenager becomes too much and the home becomes a battleground. Inevitably, the young mother has to leave and shift for herself.

Homeless and without financial support, the reality of being responsible for another human being becomes intolerable.

Welfare

In some states in the U.S.A., teenagers are able to get welfare. In Canada, she has to wait until her eighteenth birthday to get financial help.

The under-eighteen-year-old who seeks help is usually placed in a foster home with her baby. Some do well. They are able to go to school and learn a skill enabling them to become relatively self-sufficient.

The amount of welfare provided is always just enough to subsist. It means poor housing and inadequate clothing, especially in areas where winters are long and cold. It means poor nutrition, boredom, and loneliness. This frustration often leads to rejection and abuse of the children. (As we have already noted, about fifty percent of all abused children are those of single teenage parents.)

The first two or three years of life are crucial for babies. Incalculable harm can be done when the mother is unable to cope and does not nurture the baby.

Many such children end up living in group homes when they become older. Unable to cope, they act out the early deprivation by being aggressive and destructive. The more serious victims of neglect may end up in other institutions for delinquent or disturbed children.

Those mothers who continue to stay on welfare lack motivation to go back to school and attempt to become financially independent. They often drift from boyfriend to boyfriend, and end up with several children to care for alone. Alcohol, pills, and drugs often become part of their lifestyle. The children are neglected.

Schooling

The majority of pregnant teens leave school. Some girls do, however, continue their education during pregnancy. There are schools that allow pregnant girls to complete their year. The school boards in many centers offer special classes that include the regular school curriculum plus courses on nutrition and child care.

There are also homes for unwed mothers in various parts of Canada and the U.S. Girls in these homes are able to continue their education. By and large, they receive good counseling, medical care, and an opportunity to develop parenting skills. Girls generally spend about six months at the home, after which they are on their own.

Since most young mothers are untrained, the only jobs they can get— waitressing, factory work, etc.—pay poorly and involve hard, physical labor.

More ambitious, well-motivated youngsters, who try to move into better jobs, meet with opposition from employers. Once they learn that a girl has a "dependent," they refuse to hire her, believing that she will be absent too much.

One personnel director told me, "I never hire these kids, no matter how good they are or how well recommended they are. My experience has been that they are not reliable." This woman is pleasant, intelligent, and liberal-minded. She hires hundreds of girls and women, but she cannot be bothered with an employee who might cause trouble.

So the importance of a good education that will give a girl an advantage in the job market cannot be underestimated. If finishing high school and/or continuing university training is feasible, then she can avoid many of the problems we have seen in these stories. If university is

116

not possible, she can develop employment skills so that she will eventually be able to support both herself and her child in reasonable comfort.

A teenager, on her own, needs a great deal of counseling and encouragement to continue her education or to acquire job training. There are many agencies that can give a teenager the benefit of advice about the community resources available to her. (Some of these agencies are listed in Appendix One.) Financial assistance and baby-sitting services can often be arranged to aid the young mother until she becomes self-supporting.

Most single teenage parents live in cramped, inadequate quarters. A significant number are able to improve their lot and fend for themselves with some creative thinking. Some girls team up with a single mother on social assistance or one who works evenings or the night shift; one will look after the child or children during the day while the teen mother works or goes to school. This can be costly, but if the teen mother offers to sit with the woman's children during the evening, the cost can be reduced substantially.

Moving in with a male sometimes works, but more often it fails. This arrangement contributes little toward the development of the necessary skills for independence, employment, and self-sufficiency.

Another way to cope is for the teen and her child to live with a family. The teen can help with the housework as part of the cost of room and board, and a member of the family can baby-sit her child while she goes to school.

And, of course, there is always marriage, but as we have seen, few teen marriages are stable enough to weather marital storms, particularly with the added burden of a child.

Everyone needs friends, but the single parent teen needs more than most, if she is to cope with the day-to-day responsibility of caring for her child.

Friendships do much more than romances to make life less frustrating for the teen mother, but they take more work!

Friends who are sympathetic to the problems of the teenage mother can be found through discussion groups, special parenting workshops, and church groups. The young mother who involves herself in fitness and crafts programs—many of which include a component for children and are relatively inexpensive—will meet other women with similar interests and lives. The only way to lose the frustration of loneliness is to make an

117

effort to relate to people of all ages, and to become involved in activities that afford an opportunity to get out of the house, if only for one afternoon a week.

Many babies who are born sickly or underweight are prone to all sorts of illnesses. If living conditions are poor and the mother is inexperienced, problems compound.

Many conscientious teenage mothers attend lectures and workshops on parenting. They are eager and anxious to learn more about how to be an effective parent. The YWCA and similar organizations frequently offer programs dealing with these topics.

Other organizations and agencies are able to provide information and insights into the physical aspects of child care, and most are eager to lend a helping hand. Such organizations and institutions can be most helpful to the teenage mother.

19
THE WAY IT CAN BE

The problems are easily defined: too many teens are becoming pregnant and too many of those keeping their babies are ill equipped to do so. Unfortunately, the solutions are less simple.

Prevention

The key to the dilemma must be prevention. A comprehensive education program within the school system—from grade one on—should be designed to give children a sense of themselves and their need for love and attention. They must become more aware of interpersonal relationships and learn to cope within the family. Emotions such as anger and frustration must be examined and dealt with responsibly. Anatomy and physiology should be taught, and the onset of puberty and sexual awakening should be dealt with. The program should also include complete and comprehensive information on birth control methods with an emphasis on responsible behavior. Some insights into the grave responsibilities of parenthood should also be provided.

A society in which there are so many broken lives due to ignorance, violence, and inhumanity must consider alternatives. My main concern is the ever-growing army of teenager mothers—children raising children, often with tragic results.

What Can We Do?

What is needed is a realignment of available resources, greater cooperation between various health agencies and professions, and greater government support both in terms of manpower and financial commitment.

In 1978, the American government recognized the horrendous problem of teen pregnancy by establishing the office of Adolescent Pregnancy Programs through the Department of Health Education and Welfare. The aim is to set up comprehensive service centers to coordinate community health education and social services. This is designed to prevent teenage pregnancies and assist teens and teenage parents to cope with their health, education, and social problems. This is an excellent beginning.

Canada has much to do if it is to meet the problems of teenage pregnancy and parenthood head on. If it is to succeed, any program must have the support of both provincial and federal governments. The departments most directly involved are health, education, and welfare. The initial step would be the establishment of a coordinating body, including doctors who have expressed an interest in the problem (particularly obstetricians, gynecologists, and pediatricians), public health workers and representatives of community clinics, nutritionists, social scientists, educators, and representatives of health helping agencies working with teens.

The duties of this body would be many. It would be responsible for developing a prevention-oriented curriculum for use in public schools and for promoting the program to school boards, teachers, and parents. It would also be responsible for training people to present the program.

This body would develop a care program for pregnant teens to encourage proper prenatal care, and also develop and coordinate programs for those teens who decide to keep their babies. Many of these services could be delivered through existing public health units and community clinics. This group would also establish a program designed to inform teen mothers of the many problems of single parenthood and to encourage putting children up for adoption.

Every effort would be made to impress upon the young mothers the importance of prenatal classes. Whenever possible, each girl would be assigned a health worker to serve as coach during labor and delivery and as a knowledgeable friend throughout the pregnancy.

Nutrition ໄαὑ(

Under the program, doctors would refer pregnant teens to a nutritionist who would develop a diet plan for the mother. In the event that the pregnant teen is not in a residential facility, but living at home with a family unable to afford the necessary food items to meet her needs and those of the fetus, provision would be made to provide her with these items at minimal cost or free of charge depending on circumstances.

Education

Another serious problem faced by all pregnant teens is interruption of education. Schools would be encouraged (especially in small rural centers) to allow pregnant teens to attend regular classes. In larger centers, special schools could be established. In addition to the regular school curriculum, these schools would provide counseling on nutrition and parenting, and prenatal classes. Residences should be provided for students attending these schools, as "living-in" is often the only way to guarantee proper care.

Throughout the pregnancy and after giving birth, counseling should be available, not only on matters directly related to the pregnancy, but also to encourage girls to return to school; to assist them in coping with daily problems; to encourage birth control methods; and to assure them that they are not outcasts but young adults with a bright future.

Those mothers keeping their babies put added pressure on the system since they generally are not the most competent mothers. They often are forced to accept sub-standard housing, low paying jobs, and abuse from society. If we are to prevent this recurring tragedy, we must provide adequate services for the single teenage mother.

Housing

Special apartments should be built for pregnant teenagers. Teens living in these apartments would be encouraged to make every effort to become self-sufficient. They would be given an opportunity to develop skills that would allow them to compete actively in the marketplace.

These apartment buildings would include day-care facilities to allow mothers to attend classes. While living in the apartment, the girls would be taught child care and home-management skills. They would all be required to work a set number of hours in the day-care center every week. The use of drugs and alcohol would be discouraged. The buildings would also include some recreational facilities such as a pool and an exercise room.

Girls would be allowed to live in the apartments for as long as they felt a need for such an environment, or until they become both emotionally and financially able to fend for themselves.

Another type of apartment complex could be made available for girls whose babies are two or three years old. In addition to providing accommodation for single mothers and their children, there could also be apartments available for retired couples who love children and enjoy being with young people.

The couples would be carefully selected by a committee responsible for administering the buildings. A loving, caring relationship could develop between such surrogate grandparents and grandchildren, and an extended family with its sense of stability and security would develop. Old and young would be helpful to each other in a practical way, as well as providing emotional support and a sense of worth. This is one way to combat loneliness and despair for both groups.

Provision of adequate housing is one way to reduce frustration and to provide the babies and young children with an environment more conducive to good care.

Day Care

The need for more and better day care for all sectors of society is readily apparent, but the need for such services for teenage parents is acute. More day nurseries to provide care for children from infancy to five or six years of age must be established. These services will be of particular value for those mothers who have the economic and emotional stability to make their own arrangements for education or for those who have entered the work force.

Such nurseries should also include facilities to keep babies overnight for mothers who work shifts or are too ill to care for the child on their own. Strict rules about abusing this privilege would be enforced. In addition, an infirmary for children who have colds or are ill, but not ill enough to go to the hospital should be available to teenage mothers. This would greatly reduce absenteeism from school and work.

Follow-up

In addition to education and housing, a program should be established to follow up the girls and their babies for at least five years. This would include medical and nutritional counseling for both mother and child as well as parenting information sessions and, where necessary, psychological counseling for mothers.

Through these programs and services it would be possible to reduce the number of teen pregnancies. Through proper prenatal care, we would greatly reduce the number of problem-ridden, low-birth-weight infants being born to teen mothers. With comprehensive programs for single mothers, the future for both the children and their mothers will be brighter and the long-term burden placed on society will be lessened.

We must attack the problem at its source and not simply apply band-aid measures in extreme cases.

And we must begin now.

BOOKS TO READ

1. *Facts and Fancy About Birth Control, Sex Education and Family Planning.* Discusses myths and misconceptions, and gives correct information to enlighten the reader.
2. *Family Planning and Social Work.* The role of social workers in family planning and human sexuality.
3. *Family Living and Sex Education: A Guide for Parents and Youth Leaders.* Covers basic views on family, family life education, adolescent problems and marriage preparation.
4. *Approaching Adolescence.* Intended for boys entering adolescence. Discusses adolescent development in boys and girls, wet dreams, masturbation, conception, male-female relationships, sources of birth control information, V.D. information.
5. *Like It Is.* Deals with physical changes during adolescence, sexual intercourse, venereal disease, pregnancy, contraception, and abortion. Also covers teenage pregnancy from the point of view of the girl, the boy, and the parents. Discusses adoption and sources of assistance for unwed mothers.
6. *Love and Sex and Growing Up.* Talks about men and women, about their sex organs, about their roles in making and raising babies.
7. *Pregnant and Alone.* A comprehensive and up-to-date look at unwanted pregnancy and birth control.
8. *Clinical Obstetrics and Gynecology.* Evaluation and management of diseases of the vulva. Complications of teenage pregnancy. Cumulative index.

REFERENCES

"Adolescent Perinatal Health." *Am. College Obs. Gyne.*, 1979

Altchek, A., *ed.* Clinician: *Adolescent Gynecology*, 1976.

Bolognese, R.J., and Corson, S.L. "Interruption of Pregnancy." Baltimore: Williams and Wilkins, 1975.

Boyce, J. and Benoit, C. "Adolescent Pregnancy." *N.Y. State J. Med.* 75:872, 1975.

Bryan-Logan, B., and Dancy, B. "Unwed Pregnant Adolescents." *Nurs. Clin. North. Am.* 9:57, 1974.

Connell, E.B., and Jacobson, I. "Pregnancy, the Teenager and Sex Education." *Am. J. Public Health* 61:840, 1971.

Delaware Adolescent Program, Inc. (A unique comprehensive program to help pregnant teenagers.)

Dolt, A.B., and Fort, A.T. "Medical & Social Factors Affecting Early Teenage Pregnancy." *Am. J. Obs. Gyne.* 125:532, 1976.

Duenboelter, J.H., *et. al.* "Pregnancy Performance of Patients under Fifteen Years of Age." *J. Obs. Gyne.* 46:49, 1975.

Furstenberg, F. "Preventing Pregnancy among Adolescents." *Health Soc. Behav.* 12:340, 1971.

———. *Unplanned Parenthood: The Social Consequences of Teenage Childbearing.* New York: Free Press, 1976.

Gordon, L.J. *The Adolescent as Single Parent.* Milwaukee: Wisconsin Public Schools.

Grimes, D.A.; Schulz, K.F.; Cates, W., Jr.; and Tyler, C. W., Jr. Presented at the First National Medical Conference on the Safety of Fertility Control, Chicago, March, 1977.

References

Guyatt, D. *One Parent Family in Canada*. Ottawa: Institute of the Family, 1971.

Hardy, J.B., *et al.* "Long-range Outcome of Adolescent Pregnancy." *Clin. Obs. & Gyne.* 21:1215, Dec., 1978.

Hertz, D.G. "Psychological Implications of Adolescent Pregnancy: Patterns of Family Interaction in Adolescent Mothers-to-be." *Psychosomatics* 18:13. 1977.

Hornik, E. "How Teenagers, their Parents and their Doctors can all Grow Up." in Nash, E.M.; Jessner, L.; and Abse, W., eds. *Marriage Counseling in Medical Practice*. Chapel Hill: University of North Carolina Press, 1964.

Jecket, J. "Primary or Secondary Prevention of Adolescent Pregnancy." *J. Sch. Health* 47:457, 1977.

Klein, L. "Antecedents of Teenage Pregnancy." *Clin. Obs. & Gyne.* 21:1151, Dec., 1978.

Klerman, L.V., and Jekel, J.F. *School-Age Mothers: Problems, Programs and Policy*. Hamden: The Shoe String Press, 1973.

Lalonde, M. *Premature Parenthood: How Long Can We Ignore the Facts*. Planned Parenthood Federation of Canada, October 20, 1978.

MacKenzie, J.A. *Study of Unmarried Mothers*. Social Services News Department of Social Services. Halifax, Summer, 1978.

McAnarney, E.R., and Adams, B.N. "Development of an Adolescent Maternity Project in Roche, New York." *Public Health Reports*, March-April, 1977.

McAnarney, E.R., *et al.* "Obstetric, Neonatal and Psychosocial Outcome of Pregnant Adolescents." *Pediatrics*, 1978.

——— "Teenagers Evaluate Their Own Health Care." *Pediatrics*, Feb., 1975.

McAnarney, E.R., and Friedman, S.B. "Experience with an Adolescent Health Care Program." *Public Health Reports*, September-October, 1975.

Miller, W. "Psychological Vulnerability to Unwanted Pregnancy." *Fam. Plan. Perspect.* 5:199, 1973. *Opinion* 12:6, 1975.

Nadelson, C., and Notman, M.T. "Treatment of the Pregnant Teenager and the Punitive Father." *Curr. Psychiatr. Ther.* 17:81, 1977.

Nelson, R.M. "Physiologic Correlates of Puberty." *Clin. Obs. & Gyne.* 21:1137, Dec., 1978.

Osofsky, J.D., and Osofsky, J.H. "Teenage Pregnancy: Psychosocial Considerations." *Clin. Obs. & Gyne.* 21:1161, Dec., 1978.

References

Stickle, G., and Ma, P. "Pregnancy in Adolescents: Scope of the Problem." *Contemporary Obs./Gyn.* June, 1975.

Timson, J. "Teen Sex." *Maclean's,* March 31, 1980.

Tyrer, L.B., *et al.* "Meeting of the Special Needs of Pregnant Teenagers." *Clin. Obs. & Gyne.* 21:1199, Dec., 1978.

Washington Post. "Educating Future Parents." May 31, 1973.

Waters, J.L. "Pregnancy in Adolescents: A Syndrome of Failure." *South Med.* 62:655, 1969.

Zelnik, M., and Kantner, J.F. "Sexual and Contraceptive Experience of Young Unmarried Women." *Fam. Plan. Perspect.* 9:55, 1977.